MW00634613

TALLAK!

immigrant

ML Forier

Forier Press
Tucson, Arizona

Forier Press
Tucson, AZ

ISBN 978-1-7321192-0-8 Paperback

First Printing June, 2018
Reprint September, 2018

My story is created in the genre of creative nonfiction. Names have
not been changed. Places are accurate unless noted as speculative.
Events are accurate as to time and attendees, details and scenes are
often reconstructed, reflecting all items known of the event, and
adding plausible details that could have been.

To my granddaughter

Kaera Elizabeth Forier
2011 - 2013

and to the generations
of family
who preceded you
to this Hainesville hilltop

*Our lives continue — in body, mind and spirit —
from their lives. In this real sense, there is no birth
and no death. There is only the one river of life that
keeps flowing, and we all are part of it. We know that
our ancestors are not merely of a former time. They
are with us always, in our daily lives, just as we will
be in the lives of those who come after us.*

Richard Quinney
Of Time and Place

v

Preface

My story is of travel, adventure, tragedy, mystery, love and magic. I fashioned this glimpse of the lives that were lived before me, lives that touched mine, lives that shaped my foundation. It began with a taste of the old days, old ways, as a child; the memory is strong.

I was nine the day my parents dropped me into my past. Guided by my grandmother Carrie and my Uncle Oliver, I discovered their farm, a harbor of yesterday, the pump that needed priming before the water flowed, the outhouse equipped with a Sears catalog, chamber pot under my bed. I followed my uncle to the fields where he scattered the seeds from the bag on his back. I gathered the cows for the evening milking. I sat on the milking stool, examined the udder, deferred to my uncle.

My grandmother taught me how to fill the cistern from the well, how to clean the chimney and light the lamp, how to bake a biscuit in a wood stove. I lived, for a few weeks each summer, in a time before mine.

Years later I learned of the stories and family history my grandmother Carrie had written. An outline of the 100 years from my great grandmother's 1846 emigration through my grandmother's life to 1946. My cousins prepared a genealogy chart reaching back to 1750, all recorded in pre-computer days, and shared it with me. I interviewed my aunts and uncles, parents and sisters, the story getting clearer.

I combined these diverse accounts of the past. I created a website to share timelines, photos and stories. My website attracted strangers, turned cousins when we realized we shared our great-grandfather. They learned from my site as they shared their own discoveries with me.

After wrapping up my career in law firm administration, church management and consulting, I became an incurable explorer of the places and times of the 19th century. From my home in the desert of Tucson, Arizona, I explored journals and letters, parish and census records, deeds, newspapers. I traveled to the places where my ancestors strode, sailed or wagon-rode.

When my granddaughter Kaera at age two was laid to rest next to my brother, who had died when I was five, in the same plot as my grandparents and surrounded by my great grandparents, my aunts and uncles and cousins, it was all too much—there was too much history all leading to that tiny girl now a part of that story.

I wanted to see and feel and smell the life of my great-grandparents, those who began the exodus to America, those who began this tribe of Hainses and all its offshoots. I wanted to see them as clearly as my glimpse of my grandmother's life when I was nine.

And I wrote. I wrote my story. And yours.

Come with me as we visit our ancestors.

The meaning of awe is to realize that life takes place under wide horizons, horizons that range beyond the span of an individual life or even the life of a nation, a generation, or an era.

Abraham Joshua Heschel

Table of Contents

TALLAK!

immigrant

Chapter 1 — 1845 – Decisions

That rock, sprawled like a dead whale, so close he could spit on it, and did. He stood in his doorway, staring at the rock, surveying his fields, rock pulsing through some, skulking underground in others, sabotaging his crops, stifling roots.

His beautiful farm, beautiful Norway. His farm. He owned it. But it didn't matter. His farm is failing him. Norway's land has run out.

Are they right, those young rebels, Elias and his friends, that Norway is a loser, no way to expand your farm, no future for your babies?

America, they said. America

Høen Farm - 2015

He stepped back into the house, saw Ellen stretching over the cupboard for a bowl, her big belly keeping it just out of reach. Tallak walked across the room, reached for the bowl and set it on the table.

Ellen, he said, snakk med meg. Talk with me.

****

Tallak Tellifsen Høen is my great-grandfather, Ellen, his wife, my great-grandmother. One day in 1844 or 1845 this couple made the decision to leave their farm, their friends and some of their family, to travel to America.

I am the youngest daughter of the youngest daughter of the youngest son of Tallak and Ellen. The distance between us, in time and travel, is great. But I stood in the doorway of the Høen farmhouse and surveyed Tallak's fields, 170 years after his decision.

There it was, that whale of a rock on the right, a walrus-size companion on the left. I peered as Tallak might have at the fields surrounding the house, rock peeking through the grass like misplaced patio pavers, bordered with dandelions.

****

Ellen looked at his face and saw the pain. She sat with him at the table. Tallak talked of the babies to come, the baby lost. There wasn't enough food for you, he said. Gunhild didn't have a chance. Gunhild, dead in less than a month. We need to decide, he said, to start preparing now. Ellen felt the kick of the baby in her belly, felt again the pain of Gunhild's death. My baby Gunhild is buried in the Bamble cemetery, she said.

We'll bring the cradle, said Tallak.

****

2

My grandmother wrote a brief family history. Very brief. She condensed one hundred years into three pages. From her I learn:

Grandpa Tallak Haines was married in Norway to Ellen Halvorsen in about 1843. When they left for America they had one son Oliver, or Halvor. Together with them came Ellen's mother, three brothers (Elias, Ole, and Jens), and two sisters (Nellie and Kirsten). (Carrie, *History*)

Nothing more. And you, Tallak, wrote no journals, no letters. Nor you, Ellen. I cannot access your thoughts, or hear the discussions you had, but I know your decision.

I want to know you, Tallak. I want to look out of your window, Ellen, feel the shelter of your walls, the warmth of your fireplace. I want to taste your food, glimpse the stars in your skies. I want to walk where you walked.

I learned your dates and descendants from reliable family charts. I studied my grandmother's history. I discovered your names on the manifest of the barque *Sultan*, boarding in LeHavre, France and arriving in New York City in August of 1846. I gathered the parish records of the Bamble Kirke, [church] scrutinized censuses, deeds, biographies and finally newspapers to learn your movements, your interests. I quizzed my cousins, my aunts, uncles, father and sisters, prodded and poked their memories, their attics. I read the letters and journals of your fellow Norwegian emigrants.

I heard handed down stories of your kindness — to your grandchild in your very old age, to a young settler in need of help when he first arrived in the country. I witnessed the generous spirits of your grandsons and daughters, my aunts and uncles and cousins, my mother.

I gathered up the fragments. Pieced together facts and memories, travels and home places, inventions and progress. I deduced, extrapolated, dreamt.

I will tell our story to your descendants.

****

My great-grandfather Tallak was born in December of 1812 in the community of Bamble, Norway, situated in the *fylke*, or county, of Telemark. He grew up among mountains and bluffs, fjords and the waters of the North Sea. The farms of the community

were all within a radius of three to four miles. In the year 1100, the St. Olav's Kirke was built in the center of the community when the Norwegian state adopted the Christian religion. Tallak's christening, confirmation and his marriage to Ellen in 1843 were recorded in the parish records of St. Olav Kirke, but at the time Tallak and Ellen registered their names in the *Utflytte* [parish departure register] in 1846, the new Bamble Kirke had just been completed — its steeple rising high in the center of the community. The ruins of the old church remain a few hundred meters away.

The towns of Langesund and Stathelle [pronounced Stat Telle] sit on Bamble's edges. The rolling hills are covered by forests of spruce, pine, oak and lime [aka basswood or linden]; the fjords wander in from the North Sea. It seems a soft and peaceful land, but a stroll on a foot trail exposes the rock surrounding each tree; the roar of waves roiling over the rocky shores announces the savage sea. Bamble was a severe environment, breeding gristly, resolute men and women.

Tallak was his mother's firstborn son, but his father's fifth. The children born of his father's first and second wives totaled thirteen, seven sons and six daughters. Tallak had little chance of inheriting his family's farm. The firstborn son of the father would inherit (if he chose) but under the law of Odelsrett in Norway a commission fixed the value of the estate. The amount to support the widow, if any, was set aside and the rest was divided into shares — the sons received a full share, his daughters received one-half share.

The system worked better with families of less than thirteen.

Since cash was short in supply, shares were sometimes paid by slicing off a piece of the original farm, eventually creating stingy homesteads barely able to sustain one family. In 1802, there were 79,356 farms in Norway; in 1860 there were 135,000, all on that 3% of arable land that the Norwegian mountains and fjords spared.

Perhaps Tallak wasn't needed to labor on his home farm as he grew up; with four older brothers and two younger, there were more than enough hands to work the homestead. He boasted later in life that he worked on his own beginning at age fourteen, fishing on the nearby fjords, logging the still heavily wooded land and working as farmhand at harvest times. Tallak could earn only ten speciedalers in a year as a farmhand in 1840, not much to set by. [one speciedaler equaled one American dollar.]

Here my grandmother Carrie steps in with a nugget only she could tell us:

> *As a boy he* [Tallak] *worked on a farm in a settlement called Rogn ...and there he met Ellen Halvorsen.* [Halvorsdatter] (Carrie, *History*)

Ellen was a far bigger prize than the wages.

5

Chapter 2 — 1845 – Ellen

Ellen Karine Halvorsdatter was born on the farm Skjelbred, two miles from Tallak's birthplace. She was the eldest in her family of three boys and three girls. Her mother taught her to cook and bake, spin and weave, and to darn unceasingly. With her mother and soon her sisters and brothers Ellen split wood, fed and cared for the cow, pig and chickens. The men might plow, but the women harvested, scythe in hand. Ellen's brothers graduated to heavier farm chores, supervised by their father Halvor, and at age ten or eleven were off with him to log and fish and hunt. The girls stayed home and honed their household skills, becoming expert seamstresses, creative cooks, master gardeners and able food preservers, canning, drying, smoking, curing and pickling produce and butchering livestock and game. They learned the role of woman on the farm. The CEO of the homestead.

Ellen was an accomplished woman. A strong partner for Tallak.

Tallak appeared to be a good choice also. He amassed the seven hundred speciedalers to purchase the Høen farm by the time he was twenty-nine years old. An astounding feat, even for this industrious young man. His father had died in 1834, so the inheritance question had been settled. Perhaps there was a sum for Tallak after all.

However he managed, the Høen farm was his in 1842, and in July of 1843 Ellen Karine Halvorsdatter and Tallak Tellefsen married, she twenty-six, he thirty, the event duly recorded in the Bamble Kirke parish records. Then a baby — their daughter, Gunhild Kirstine, born in October, so soon, so beautiful. Tallak and Ellen had chosen to delay their marriage until the Høen farm belonged to Tallak — engagements were often long and frustrating, and early babies were neither surprising nor scorned in Norway.

Ellen had been hearing of the glories of emigration for years from her brother Elias, three years her junior. He and his friend Lars, twenty-three-year-olds, announced their intention to leave for America in April of 1843. They even signed the *Utflytte* register in the Bamble Kirke. They didn't leave then, from lack of funds or parental disapproval, but after that failure they changed tactics, urging those disapproving parents and their families to join them in their preposterous scheme. Elias targeted first his mother Marte, then Tallak, knowing that his mother wouldn't go without her eldest daughter, and Ellen and Tallak were a team. Elias read or listened to every letter from America he could find, and shared all the good parts with his family; luckily most letters were positive. He and his friend Lars didn't stop there. They made sure that everyone in the village knew of the acres and acres available, virgin land, virgin forests, unspoiled, unmapped and available for a song.

Elias's two brothers, Jens, twenty, and Ole, thirteen, were ready to go. Of the girls, the two oldest, Kirsten and Nella, were easy to convince, too. They were working harder than ever with Ellen married and gone. Their brothers, also working long hours logging and fishing, came home expecting evening chores done, dinner on the table, warmth and comfort in their home. The girls saw their future clearly: marrying the boy next door and struggling for existence on a farm they owned or rented as husman, hired to work on the owner's farm with a small cottage and plot of land for sustenance.

Helene, Ellen's youngest sister, age thirteen, lived and worked on a neighboring farm, a customary practice for girls in Norway. The family she lived with, Lars and Kari Vinje, had no children, making it easy for a close bond to develop between the couple and their hired girl. Helene could be the daughter they never had.

Helene was not leaving.

Marte, mother of them all, hesitated as her youngest child declared her intent to stay in Norway. But she knew the Vinjes were good people, and she had five other children to consider. Would they stay in Norway if she declined? Or just go without her? Her only grandchild would be on this trip, if he lived. And she wanted to see what this new country was like, this new home of her children and grandchildren. Her son-in-law, Tallak, thirty-two years old, was the elder of the younger generation, experienced, enterprising, a doer. He and her son Elias would lead them. With the proceeds from the sale of Marte's farm and Tallak's, the journey ahead would be well-funded. Marte, Ellen and Tallak were the anchors of this adventure. The children would go.

Marte must go.

The men were restless . . . the women were eager . . . their traditions would not feed the family.

A decision must be made.

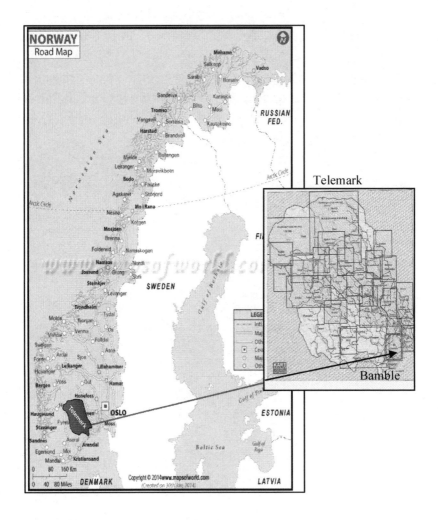

Chapter 3 — 1845 – Preparation

Elias and his friend Lars won the day. Elias's mother Marte elected to leave her country with her older children. Tallak ripped himself from his land; Ellen and their healthy son Halvor would go with the now occupied cradle, and the rocking chair too. Ellen's two sisters and three brothers rejoiced. Lars had persuaded his own family to emigrate, and four additional Bamble families were packing up.

Helene stayed steadfast in her decision. She made her home with the Vinje's in Norway.

****

I have already mentioned that my grandmother Carrie's compact history is my guide, the skeleton of this story, my bridge to my great-grandparents. She was close to eighty when she wrote her memories down. Her daughter, my Aunt Petra, transcribed the short stories to create a history of our family. Carrie wrote first what she remembered being told, possibly by her father-in-law Tallak himself. As she became a player in the story, she wrote of her own memories.

Grandma Carrie's history is in harmony with the facts I've collected over the years. Except . . .

> *Another sister, Hellene, was left in Norway. She was about seven years old and was adopted by an old couple, Lars and Kari Vinje.*

My grandmother's description of Hellene [Helene] as seven years old and "left in Norway" caused great consternation among us descendants early on. "How could they just leave poor little Helene in Norway." "How cruel," we contemporary cousins would agree. Happily, Bamble parish research revealed Helene's age in 1846 as fourteen, not seven. We were still concerned, until learning how common it was in Norway for young girls to work as live-in hired help, and of course, the Vinjes did adopt the child. We all relaxed.

The leaving was permanent. The travel was to the unknown and through the unknown, except for the knowledge that it would be long and arduous, requiring endurance and coping and resourcefulness. This was the largest group to be leaving Bamble together; only twelve people had previously emigrated to America, one small group each in the years 1844 and 1845. Never had so many made this bold decision.

An agent of the ocean-sailing barque *Sultan* of the port of LeHavre, France, must have gotten wind of the emigration fever sweeping the county of Telemark. The arrival of the agent, with his practiced sales pitch, may have convinced more families to emigrate. One happy agent filled his ship with ninety-two passengers, thirty-two from Bamble, the remaining from the neighboring municipalities of Drangedal and Sandal, all in Telemark County.

Norway offered few ocean passages for emigrants in 1846. Steady trade began around 1850, when Norway doubled its iron exports to America, and shipping lines bragged of "emigrants and iron riding the same keels."

Getting to LeHavre would take some planning — first to arrange travel from Norway to LeHavre, then from Bamble to that Norwegian launching point. Did the travel agent help to arrange that transfer? Its timeliness would be crucial.

In spring of 1845, both the Høen and Røsklev lands were stretched to their limits with expanded garden plots and doubled wheat and barley fields. Enough to feed them all through winter and spring, the voyage and beyond. Marte and Ellen supervised their separate gardens, with Ole and Jens manning the plows, Kirsten, Nella, and maybe even Helene sowing all the cabbage, peas and beet seeds they could find. They quartered and then re-quartered last year's potatoes to extend their output. This had to be the best crop ever. Tallak, Elias, Jens and Ole fished, trapped and hunted. The women fattened pigs, cows, nurtured the piglets and calves.

The men felled the oak trees to make the long-grained boards for barrel and keg construction, then turned that job over to the best cooper in the community. The lumberjacks of the family might hire on to logging teams through the winter. Each speciedaller stashed away for the journey eased their collective anxiety.

The families had etched in their minds the list of provisions required by the shipping company for the two-month plus journey across the Atlantic:

> . . .*kitchen utensils and provisions for 10 weeks. [For] each grown person: 70 pounds of bread, 8 pounds of butter, 24 pounds of meat, 10 pounds of pork, 1 keg of herring, 3/8 barrel of potatoes, 20 pounds of rye or barley flour, 1/2 skjeppe (ca. 1/4 bushel) peas, 1/2 skjeppe pearled barley, 3 pounds of coffee, 3 pounds of sugar, 2 1/2 pounds of syrup, and a little salt, pepper, vinegar, and onions.*

Multiply by nine adults. A lot of food to muster. But the voyage was long, the sea air brisk, young appetites hearty; they would be thankful if the food lasted to New York. The skipper provided three potter (about three quarts) of water for each passenger per day.

By spring of 1846, the dust was flying all over Bamble. The Høens and Halversens, Langetangens, Fjellesteds, Midgaardens, Herums — the names just roll off your tongue — all cleaning house, making lists, sorting and packing. It was time to butcher the pigs and calves and dry, salt or can their cache. They brought any excess produce to market to trade for coffee, sugar and salt. The women baked the flatbread, unleavened, rolled thin, on a griddle over an open fire, and packed it into the kegs; they canned their churned butter and wrapped the cheese. They sold their horse or oxen and carts and sleds, with the provision that ownership be delayed, allowing the sellers to use the animals and carts for the journey to their Norway port.

They sold furniture and farm machinery, tools and kitchen utensils, clothes, linens, family heirlooms, cherished possessions, anything that couldn't journey with them and wasn't left with their farms.

They packed Sunday Best for the hoped-for Sunday services on board. The women wove and knit the necessary clothes or linens, mended and darned worn clothes with invisible stitches. Trunks were filled with logging and fishing tools, farm implements, seeds to plant in a new land. Tallak disassembled the rocking chair, spinning wheel and baby cradle. Pots and pans and chamber pots were carefully wrapped and stowed for their new home. In America.

Ellen's family had moved from the Skjelbred farm to Røskleven sometime before Helene was born. When Ellen's father died, the Røskleven farm passed to his widow Marte, who had the legal authority to sell the property, with the proviso that she has a male legal advisor of age twenty-five or older. Her son Elias, barely twenty-five, may have been her advisor. Marte, as a widow, enjoyed more property rights than any other class of women in Norway, single or married. Still . . . I suspect it rankled to ask her son to be her legal advisor so that she could sell her own land. She realized four hundred speciedalers for the sale. Tallak completed the sale of the Høen farm to Ole Finmark and pocketed seven hundred speciedallers.

Finally, on May 9, 1846, the family visited the parish pastor to register their names in the *Utflytte*:

.

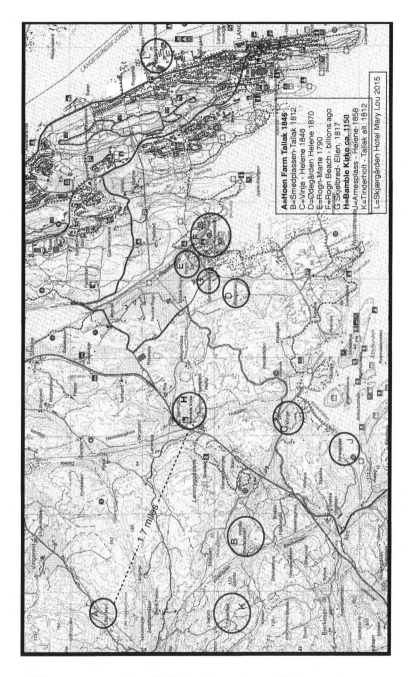

Ellen twenty-nine, Tallak thirty-three, Halvor, almost two, Ellen's mother Marte, age fifty-six, and her children, Mikael Jens, twenty-four, Kirstine Gurine, twenty-one, Nella Oline, nineteen, Ole, fifteen. Record our destination as America, they said. America.

Elias, who had registered his intent to leave for America in 1843, did not register again. But just one month before the family left Norway Elias married Berthe Marie Henriksdatter. It's all there, first in the marriage record, then the *Utflytte* register (Berthe's name between Marte and Kirsten) and finally on the *Sultan* ship's manifest immediately below Elias's name. She walked off the ship in New York on Elias's arm. But that is the last we hear of her; neither her name nor a first marriage for Elias is mentioned by Grandma Carrie. Nonetheless, Berthe was there in 1846, and the traveling family group increased to ten.

Helene's name would not appear in those records until 1882. She would never see her sister Ellen again, but she would reunite with her aging siblings far in the future.

Tallak left his mother, six brothers and six sisters in Norway. His family is not involved in Tallak's adventures, but Monica, a fourth generation descendent of his step-brother who remained in Norway, will connect with this writer over a hundred years later and will guide me through the Bamble locations where our ancestors lived.

Each traveler fashioned a kit of his or her mattress, quilts and personal items. Knitting needles, whittling tools, bibles and prayer books, precious things— slipped into the kits before the job was done.

Someone in the family marked the kegs and barrels with names and destination, then marked each to identify which containers held food and items needed on the voyage, and which could be stored deep in the hold, the treasures to be unpacked someday, somewhere, when there was a home again.

The packing was done.
Time to say goodbye.

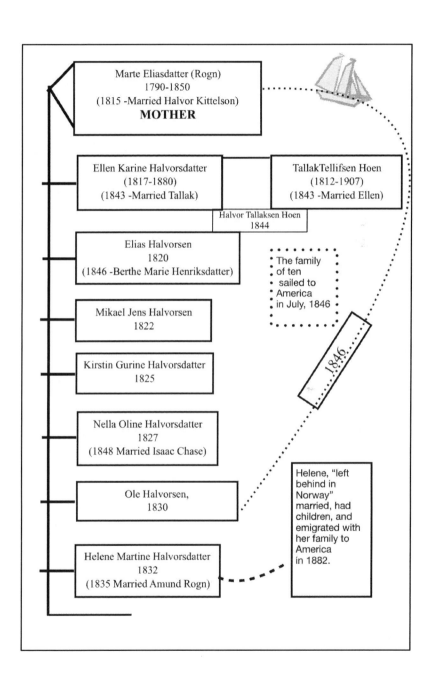

Marte Eliasdatter (Rogn)
1790-1850
(1815 -Married Halvor Kittelson)
MOTHER

Ellen Karine Halvorsdatter
(1817-1880)
(1843 -Married Tallak)

TallakTellifsen Hoen
(1812-1907)
(1843 -Married Ellen)

Halvor Tallaksen Hoen
1844

Elias Halvorsen
1820
(1846 -Berthe Marie Henriksdatter)

The family
of ten
sailed to
America
in July, 1846

Mikael Jens Halvorsen
1822

Kirstin Gurine Halvorsdatter
1825

Nella Oline Halvorsdatter
1827
(1848 Married Isaac Chase)

1846

Ole Halvorsen,
1830

Helene, "left
behind in
Norway"
married, had
children, and
emigrated with
her family to
America
in 1882.

Helene Martine Halvorsdatter
1832
(1835 Married Amund Rogn)

17

TALLAK! immigrant

Chapter 4 — 1846 – The Leaving

Six families, men and women, the oldest age sixty-five, the youngest two months, and several loners, all men. Did they gather at the Bamble Kirke that morning? Their carts fully loaded, their hearts pulled tight?

Friends and families of the emigrants, the tearful, the curious, a few tut-tutting, mingled with the group. This coterie was the largest group of emigrants to leave Norway so far, a portentous event. What did this exodus of these vigorous and bold neighbors mean for the future of Bamble? Who would leave next?

Bamble Kirke
1843 - Today

Children ran around and through the gathering carts and people, romping with friends, none quite aware of the separation about to happen. The horses and oxen stomped and snorted, their harnesses jingling. The hardy few who were pulling their carts with manpower hefted the handles, testing the weight once again.

Helene, determined not to cry, probably cried anyway. She would stick to her decision, and yet … her entire family was leaving. She clung to Lars and Kari for support, practicing a smile for her siblings as they began their journey. Perhaps Tallak's mother, a brother or sister, came to wish son and brother Godspeed. Would their parish pastor join them to give a blessing for this traveling group? The official Norwegian Lutheran

Church was opposed to emigration, considering it the work of the devil. But this local pastor had baptized these errant parishioners, confirmed and married many, buried the spouses of the oldest and too many babies. This local pastor might have understood the bad times his parishioners had been through, and quietly rejoiced in their lust for life.

I do hope this churchman blessed the journey of my forebears.

The carts and wagons lurched grudgingly into movement, the caravan was formed, the good byes said, the thirty-four men, women and children began the journey.

Oh! the excitement! The exultation, knotted stomachs, freedom, tears, the prayers. They were on their way!

A ship sailed from Porsgrunn to LeHavre on May 12, 1846 — the timing was right to transport this group to the French port in plenty of time. Porsgrunn (twelve miles) was likely the furthest they needed to travel, ships might have stopped at the even closer ports of Brevik or Stathelle. Even with the heavy loads, their trek would take no more than an unhurried day. Relatives and lifetime friends walked with the group, talking of weather and neighborhood gossip as on any ordinary day, delaying the forever goodbyes a little longer. The road curved, rose and fell, lined with daisies, dandelions, a point of white just beginning to emerge from the deep green leaves of the *liljekonval* [lily of the valley]. Ellen might fall behind to gather a few of the newly sprouted herbs to tuck away in her pocket — a brightener for the simple food packed for the journey.

The conversations eased away, slipped into silence. Even the children softened their steps. The rumble of hooves and carts remained, louder as the roadbed became rock, softened as the road returned to earth, easy wheel-tracks to follow. Cows grazed in the green fields they passed, a few calves cavorting in the grass. The lilac bushes bloomed gloriously purple at the edges of the fields. Often rocks bordered the road, but softened by the moss turned spring-green and the sprigs of new bushes, trees, bursting from each crevasse.

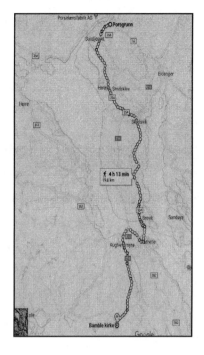

The road was familiar to those who had traded in the port towns in the past. This trip took longer, with all the children and older folks, with the oxen and horses pulling heavy loads. This trip took longer, as the commonplace turned mystical, transformed, whispering good-bye.

They reached the Frierfjord; to continue to Brevik or Porsgrunn the men and their animals and carts must cross the fjord on a flatboat. Women and youngsters beat them in rowboat-ferries, all meeting again on the northern bank. It might take many crossings to trundle the six families and their possessions across.

After the Frierfjord crossing, the caravan continued on to the dock on the Langesundfjorden in their town of departure. Was the ship waiting when they arrived? If not, they would store their trunks and barrels on the dock and find a place of lodging to wait for the ship.

The final goodbyes must be said. The travelers released the wagons and horses to the care of the neighbors and kin to return to Bamble. They faced each other, shook hands, wished each other well; those on the left returned to their familiar Bamble, those on the right looked to the sea.

The travelers from Drangedal and Sandal, heading for Le Havre and the same sailing ship to America, might gather at the dock with the Bambleingers. Some may have met before on market days over the years. No matter, they would soon know each other well — intimately, considering their communal living quarters for the next two months or so.

The brig arrived, boasting two masts, square rigged, and small enough to maneuver in the fjord, a slightly smaller vessel

than the barque they would be traveling on when crossing the ocean. The crew loaded the barrels and kegs on the ship, and children, mothers and fathers, grandmothers and grandfathers climbed the gangplank to find their places. This trip would take about five days — a practice run for the longer voyage ahead.

They plunked their carry-ons down on the deck. Were there berths below? Or was this a freight ship, redirected to carry this load of Norwegians to France? Sleeping on deck might be the preferable option — not unusual in these early emigration days.

They sailed 691 nautical miles, down the Langesundfjorden and into the Skagerak strait to the North Sea, soon cruising past the southern tip of Norway. They sailed past Denmark, Germany and the Netherlands, and finally into the English Channel and to the port of Le Havre.

Le Havre—a major port city with a population of thirty thousand —was bigger than any place these rural families had seen. The scene of the waiting place is described by the French historian Andre Corvisier:

. . . The less fortunate [emigrants] sleep in the street, on the floor, or in makeshift tents on the banks of the streets and sidewalks of St. Francis and Notre Dame. Others took refuge in shacks close to the fortifications or in the plain with their baggage. In 1840, the "Revue du Havre" wrote that "the city is crowded with the poorest . . . immigrants ... they take shelter under the elms; excavations in the thickness of slope ditches serve as their home. . . Those who have two francs a day, can find accommodation among innkeepers of St. Francis and Our Lady, who specialize in taking care of immigrants. . .

Would our traveling group risk spending funds so early in the journey? Perhaps instead these ninety-two Norwegians banded together and found an empty spot for themselves and their belongings on the plains and camped under the elm trees, thankful for the comradeship of their Norsk neighbors.

They waited a month or so, or perhaps just a few weeks. They had signed the Bamble Parish *Utflytte* record in May and a family record asserts that they left Bamble in that month. The ship manifest states that the *Sultan* left LeHavre on June 26, 1846. Exactly when the ship arrived in port, and when the passengers were allowed to board, is uncertain. But they were spared the long wait that some emigrants experienced — of many months or even a year in their port of departure. Savvy travelers, these Norwegians. Or lucky beginners.

One day in June 1846 they boarded the sailing ship *Sultan*, bound for New York City, America, and waited for the wind.

Chapter 5 — 1846 – All Aboard

Ellen carried Halvor up the gangplank, looking at the deck above her, estimating the height of the railing against the height of this small wriggling boy in her arms. Halvor was eager to try out his walking skills honed on the streets of Le Havre. Marte worried her way forward too, wondering how Ellen would cope with her lively two-year-old, wondering how she and her older bones would fare on this journey, already feeling endless. Tallak and Elias, Jens and Ole tramped up in the rear, carrying multiple mattress kits, helping their womenfolk. Each of them felt relief and anxiety mixed in a stomach-lurching formula as they finally boarded the ship *Sultan*.

****

The *Sultan* was listed as "barque" on the Lloyd's Register of 1846, carrying three or four masts, square sails and triangular. She weighed 287 ton.

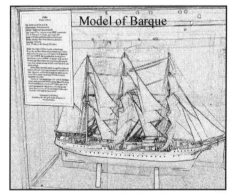

Model of Barque

The ship's crew hustled them forward, onto the deck and then down the tight stairs of the companionway. The cabin midsection held the family bunks, advertised as enough space for five persons. No dimensions given. Curtains might hang between sections with the sign "Single Women" tacked on the forward curtain and "Single Men" on the aft. But no time to gawk. They were pushed forward as their fellow emigrants scrambled down the companionway behind them. Tallak and Ellen found their family bunk, and threw their belongings on it. Elias and Berthe grabbed a top tier, following advice for avoiding the possible seasick upchuck emerging from a neighbor above.

Marte, with Kirsten and Nella, moved toward the Single Women section — double rows of bunks along each wall, each two feet wide, six feet long and with about two and a half feet between the upper and lower bunk. The passageway narrowed as it went forward. They chose their space quickly, but carefully, it would be their only "private" space in the months ahead. They would share their quarters with six additional women.

Jens and Ole scrambled for their bunks in the Men's Section, guiltily looking forward to some seclusion from their mom and sisters. Their section would eventually be filled with eighteen men, ages fourteen to fifty-four.

The family gathered again in the central cabin when all passengers were on board. The crew was wrestling with the trunks, lowering them one at a time, none too gently, somewhat like today's airline baggage handlers, I suspect. Elias and Tallak shifted their trunks to the right spaces, Jens and Ole helped any passengers who needed it — so many families, so many trunks! The sailors announced that the food supplies brought aboard by each family would be accessible on deck (at least in fair weather) and each family could keep one trunk close to their bunk.

Ellen, as the oldest sibling, married and mothering, took the leadership role with the group of women, dividing the anticipated chores with her younger sisters. Marte was the senior, but at her age perhaps honorary, not acting matriarch. But the women were all curious to see the communal kitchen. Where would they heat their food? Where was the wood stored? Was there a reservoir for water, or did the crew dole out the promised three potter per person each day? Cooking, washing up, watching over the babies, keeping things tidy, caring for the sick, all in strange facilities, shared with ninety-two individuals. That was the women's work. Still, the realization of the impending recess from many chores was dawning on them. No cows to feed

26

and milk, no lambs to birth, no wood to chop and split for the fire.

The men had an even greater change in their workday. There was no workday. No logging, no plowing, no fishing, except for the times when the occasional ocean reef allowed an hour or two of salt sea trawling. Men did not cook. They steered clear of the sickbeds. Women's work, all of it. The young fathers might be some help in watching over the babies . . . who could resist the comical stride of a one year old learning to walk on the deck of a barque?

But it was the children who felt a freedom never known in their short lifetimes. Children from four years to twelve were relieved of just about all their chores. Some harried parents were sending them off on errands around the ship . . . find the water barrel, take this shawl to grandmother, hang, no, tie the baby's wrappings on the rail so they don't blow off. But running around the ship for any chore was more fun than mucking out the barn. They had already found nooks and crannies that not one parent knew about, and most sailors were tolerant of an idle child lurking in a below decks hideaway. It was glorious!

The ship's manifest listed the occupation of all the men as farmers except for one blacksmith, one shoemaker, one carpenter and one servant. A convenient description, farmers, describing the fact that these men lived on farms, but hardly depicting the major occupation of these Norwegians. They were loggers or fishermen; some mined, some hunted. Men's farm-work included the plowing and butchering and threshing, but the women ran the farm, and did all the daily work. These women weren't hoeing a hobby garden, but a carefully planned sustenance garden. They spread seed in the fields and often scythed the grown grain, that and the produce from garden, orchard and wild berries had to last an entire year. The occupation column for women was blank.

No passenger on the *Sultan* listed the occupation of doctor. The captain or a special crew member on board would fill that role, if needed, but the women on board could provide the home remedies these families regularly depended on. It would suffice. Must suffice.

The boat would sail when the wind was right, allowing the passengers time to acclimate to their seagoing home for a few days or more. Halvor, with Ellen's help, discovered seven playmates, all between two and four. That meant plenty of company for Ellen, too, mothers galore! Ingeborg Andersdatter, four daughters ages six to two months; Johanne Lynne, six children ages twenty-one to two-year-old twins; Sara Nielsdatter, five children, the youngest four and two, and Karen Henriksdatter, Berthe's sister, with a four-month-old baby. These mothers were gauging the on-deck space, estimating what it would take to prevent their active toddlers from falling overboard.

The two babies added an extra burden for their mothers. The interior wrap — close to the baby's bottom — of their swaddling clothes required regular replacing. With the limited water supply and washing facilities, swaddling clothes were often simply dried and re-used. Halvor toddled around in a dress-like garment, helpful in developing toilet habits. A good thing he was familiar with a bucket for that purpose, since the ship lavatories, one for the women and one for the men, were busy all day. A shipboard slop-jar came in handy. It's easy to picture Tallak teaching Halvor to hold on tight and pee to leeward off the ship's deck.

The travelers weren't on board too many days before Tallak and those many sea-savvy men felt the wind shift, noticed a stiff wind blowing out at sea, and watched as the ship came alive with sailors climbing the masts, releasing lines, shouting commands.

Tugboats, if needed, were rowed by accomplished boatmen, with spring lines attached to the tugboat and the *Sultan*, the boatmen maneuvering the stern or bow to a favorable wind position with winch and muscle. In easier harbors the spring lines were attached to the ship fore and aft and manipulated from the dock. But the best exit, the maneuver skippers preferred above all others, was to call off the tugboat and dock helpers, set the sails and put out to sea. No assistance, just skill . . . and the right wind.

They would set their feet on land once again in fifty-six days

Chapter 6 — 1846 – The North Atlantic

The good ship *Sultan* depended on the velocity and direction of the wind, along with the versatility of its sails and the skills of its sailors, for the speed of the journey. Its sails — mainsail, topsail, topgallant, jib, flying jib, foresail, stern top, stern topgallant, lee and staysails — seldom flying all at once, but magnificent when the wind allowed. The Captain determined how much sail would fly; the wind directed the Captain. The sailors lowered or raised each sail by hand, climbed the mast for sail adjustments, scuttled out on the crossbar to adjust lines and lashings and secure with just the right knot.

One day the emigrants enjoyed a smooth sail — the ship skimming the surface of the sea with all sails flying — and on another found it difficult to walk a step without clutching line or railing, deck rails close to the sea, falling overboard a distinct possibility.

Or the wind might disappear, leaving the ship victim of the waves and swells with an unpredictable motion, the worst for seasickness. A contrary wind could blow relentlessly in the wrong direction, requiring tacking back and forth and back and forth with no discernible progress — especially if you can see the land just left behind or the land you long to set your feet on.

And then there were the gales, with just a few reefed sails up, the sturdy vessel reduced to a play toy of the sea, tossing and lurching, everyone huddled in the below-deck quarters holding on, just holding on.

Were they seasick on those first days? Most first-time ocean sailors experience at least a day or two of this disagreeable initiation as their body acclimates to the subtle movements of the ship. When the gales hit, even the hardiest feel the swirling of the stomach, its expulsion of lunch in the wrong direction, slowly rising, rising, no, not now, where's my burp cup, where's the chamber pot, wait . . .. *Jævli*! [damn].

****

I sailed the North Atlantic on the *Bergensfjord*, from New York City to Stavanger, Norway in 1970, the fading days of ocean liner passenger ships. The Bergensfjord weighed 18,000 tons, sixty times the 287 tons of the *Sultan*, and powered by a twentieth century steam engine carrying us from continent to continent in seven days. But a gale blew in three hours after we left the New York dock, before any of us had our sea legs, tossing that ship as if it were a balloon bouncing through the waves. We called them "burp cups" and the crew placed one on every other step on the multiple stairways, every six feet in the hallways. My husband was one of six passengers who enjoyed dinner and a movie that evening; the kids and I, despite magic modern medicine, were in our bunks, holding on, just holding on.

****

There were days on deck, and days below. Good days and bad.

It was a good day — a day on deck to enjoy the sun, to visit with fellow emigrants. The fiddler pulled his hardingfele, the traditional Hardanger fiddle of Norway, from his fiddle case, and began a Halling tune, a fast, sharp folk dance. A few young folks — there were eighteen between the ages of sixteen and twenty-five — stepped a Halling, as they put it, on any deck-space available. Ellen and the other mothers stepped to a different beat, the dance of their toddlers' feet running toward one calamity after another, the moms taking turns guarding the rails. Marte and the older women knit and crocheted, talked of their homeland and their family, each relieved to be on deck after several days of stormy below-deck time. Marte scanned the dancers to see if her daughter Kirsten was among them. She and

Soren Anderson had disappeared a few times, courting, she assumed, although where they would find an alone place on this crowded ship was a puzzle.

Tallak and the men smoked their pipes, speculating about their future in the new world. What comes next, when we step out on the land? Ellen slipped over to hear their talk, to add a few ideas, perhaps to join them in smoking as she lit up her own pipe. They sat on boxes and barrels and spread their quilts and wet clothes over any space available to dry out in the wondrous sunshine.

On the balmiest of the on-deck days, families enjoyed the noontime dinner on deck. Small boys and girls ran pell-mell down the companionway to gather eating utensils and bowls from the cabin below. The women dished out their jointly prepared barley, pork and potato stew, passed the *flatbrød, smør og ost* [flatbread, butter and cheese], potluck style, among newfound friends on board.

Washing up after dinner might well be similar to an 1888 voyage described in *A Sham Immigrant's Voyage to New York*:

> *By the direction of the sailors we scraped our potato skins and other debris over the ship's side. The galley cook filled a tub with hot water on the lee deck close by the rail. About this we stood in circles six deep waiting for a chance to rinse our platters. When my turn arrived the water was cold and diversified with archipelagoes of potato and meat.*

Even the luxury of hot water for cleaning up might not be considered on this 1846 voyage. Perhaps a bucket of cold salt water must suffice.

Dolphins occasionally appeared on these days to entertain them, or even whales "bigger than a cow," a formerly land-locked farmer noted. "Reef!" the sailors would call out on the best of days, and Tallak, Elias, Ole and Jens, skillful fjord and North Sea fishermen, tried their hand at north Atlantic reef fishing. The fresh-caught whitefish or cod, routine fare in their homeland, tasted like the rarest delicacy after weeks of salt herring and dried meat.

Then there were the tolerable days below-deck, with wind or rain or simple sun fatigue, or sailors ordering everyone below for a deck- cleaning day. Mothers and aunts might teach the littlest to crochet, or knit, and set the older children to improve their advanced stitchery skills; was there a teacher on board to introduce reading or writing? Whittling could occupy the men and boys, a soup ladle or spoons for the table. The youngest were entertained by *bestemor* [grandmother] stories, oral tales, by Marte and her two elder friends. Every child needed a grandmother, and many had left theirs behind in Norway.

Dinner was simple fare on below-deck days, hardtack and herring perhaps, all set out on their trunks turned table for the meal. Coffee was in their list of supplies — was hot water available below-deck?

When the Captain ordered all hatches closed, imprisoning the emigrants in their quarters — those were the bad below-deck days. The days when most of the people were sick, chamber pots and buckets overflowing, when even the sea-hardy few lacked the grit to clean up.

No dinner that day or night . . . Or days and nights.

They were holding on, just holding on.

Did these hardy emigrants get used to the cramped quarters, the lack of privacy, the obstacles to daily routines? They waited in line to use the privy, cook their meals, rinse their plates or to get a drink of water. When sick, they were sick in the middle of a crowd. A bath, even in the Victorian method of bathing each section of the body while fully clothed, was taken in the crowded communal bathroom, or worse, in the main cabin with all souls present. Was there water enough for bathing?

Space and privacy limitations might hinder opportunities for intimacy as well, a mixed blessing. Abstinence was the only reliable method of birth control, and since the journey for most families would continue well beyond this ocean crossing, women might find pregnancy inconvenient and downright uncomfortable. Ellen did not have another child until December of 1847, three and a half years after the birth of Halvor, an atypical time between pregnancies. Halvor was still nursing on this crossing, a practice which, in addition to its convenience and efficiency, was considered a hindrance to pregnancy. It didn't always work, but most women of the time managed to space their children to every two years.

Tallak, Ellen, Halvor, and Ellen's family were emigrating early in the heyday of northern European emigration. The ninety-two passengers on the *Sultan* included neighbors and friends; they all spoke the same language. Some of the privations that seem intolerable today were not too different from daily life at that time. Even the food that they carried onto the ship was about the same as what they ate during the long winter months — all canned or dried or salted, frozen if weather permitted, or aging well or badly in the cellar. Fish was eaten fresh only on the day it was caught. The excess catch was immediately salted.

You and me? We would have a hard time existing anywhere in 1846.

With luck, the voyage offered a varied sailing experience, with just a few days locked up below with stormy seas, and many days of full sails with steady winds. They made the trip in eight weeks, close to the minimum length of a crossing at the time.

Ninety-two boarded the ship in Le Havre and ninety-two walked down the gangway in New York. There were no deaths or births recorded in the ship's log. It's a good sign that the trip was on the shorter side of the spectrum of ocean sailing vessels of the time. Maybe it is also a good sign that few tales were passed down of this momentous exploit. It could be that these emigrating pioneers experienced this voyage as just a part of life, not extraordinary. I think they could take it. And there was much more to come.

Captain Bussan certified their arrival on the *Sultan* manifest: "Arrived in New York on August 14, 1846, having left 56 days earlier, with 92 passengers.

Chapter 7 — 1846 – New York, New York

The hush, and yet the hubbub — these were the contradictions of arriving in the New York harbor. Passengers and sailors gathered on deck. The canvas aloft was minimal, just enough sail to maintain course. Captain Bussan wove the *Sultan* through the hundreds of sailing ships, fewer steamships, some anchored and some moving ghostlike toward or away from the busy docks. The harbor waters were calm, the crashes of waves against the hull were stilled, the deck eerily flat, the ship suddenly cathedral-like, a quietness not heard or felt in eight weeks. But the tumult of the sea was replaced by the cacophony of ship masters shouting orders, harbormasters in rowboats yelling to ask permission to come aboard, gulls and terns, kittiwakes and skimmers, whirling and screeching and diving for debris. Then the sounds of the city began wafting toward their ears, beginning as a low homogenous hum, transforming into isolated voices of hawkers and horses and cobblestones and travelers with feet on solid land, the glorious babble of lower Manhattan, New York City, America.

There was no Statue of Liberty in the harbor to welcome these immigrants. There was no Ellis Island or Castle Garden to ease their landing in America. The spire of Trinity Church greeted them, the tallest structure in Manhattan, its third rebuilding completed that very year.

The family and their fellow passengers were about to step onto the land of America. Good health was the only requirement for entry. No passport, no work permit. Their health was certified by the officer, who boarded the ship and checked each passenger, watched for coughing, rashes, miserableness. Looked closely at eyes, nose, tongue. "Welcome, immigrants!

Now off you go . . ."

Ships lined the East River docks, loading and unloading cargo and people. The *Sultan* sailed to a stop at one of those docks on Friday, August 14, 1846. Tallak and Ellen with Halvor between them, Nella, Ole, Kirstin, Jens and their mother Marte walked down the gangplank and into their future. Berthe walked with her husband Elias. Berthe walked into obscurity.

The family pressed together, rallied round their fellow Bamblingers, all somewhat shaky on their legs as the land rolled beneath them. Were they dressed in their Sunday best? Certainly. Marte wore her high-necked, long-sleeved, many-buttoned bodice, her corset assuring a smooth fit, shoes barely visible beneath her long skirts. Her daughters' attire matched hers, even teenaged Nella wore the same strict costume. The men looked just as formal in their black jackets, vests, white shirts and black bow ties.

Toddler Halvor, dressed in his own jacket and skirt, long stockings and black shoes, was straining for freedom. Ellen was just as determined not to let him loose in this hubbub. Marte hovered nearby, her eyes also on her grandson. The rest of the family stood transfixed, pondering the scene. Every one of them was as excited as Halvor, with the adult overlay of panic. How strange everything seemed!

Scavenging gulls scrabbled, still screeching, horses and carriages clattered on the cobblestone streets, hawkers shouted:

Book the Knickerbocker, sailing the Hudson twice a day.
Hackney Carriages - Take a tour of the city.
Wagons here — easy transport to steamboats.

Dutch, Irish, English, Belgian, Norwegian, German, trying to understand and be understood, and talking louder and louder to help it along. The blended aromas of horse droppings, garbage and people added to the drama.

The New York *Evening Post* issue of that day noted that two thousand steerage passengers had arrived from foreign ports on the previous Tuesday, and another seven hundred fifty by Wednesday noon.

Suddenly the Bamblelingers heard something standing out from the cacophony — their language! How welcome the sound was amid of all this strangeness. What were they saying?

Bestill Knickerbocker, seiling Hudson på 19.
Omvisning på City of New York.
Vogner her - beste priser til dampbåter.

Hawkers! Same advertising, different language. Now they knew what all that shouting was about. Shipboard discussions had alerted the *Sultan* passengers of the hazards of the hawker-rogues, no matter what language. Norwegian swindlers, recent immigrants themselves but mostly outright crooks doing their best to rob their countrymen of any funds they possessed. The hawkers were aggressive, earning their living as agents of steamboat and hotel and railroad tycoons. *But surely these familiar young men could mean us no harm . . .*

****

Did my family resist the hawking? Did they have their own plan of action when they stepped onto American soil? Did they know where they were headed?

The pathway chosen by the majority of Norwegian immigrants in 1846 was from New York City to Troy, New York via steamboat, then to Buffalo via the Erie Canal and from Buffalo via the Great Lakes to Wisconsin or Chicago. It was also the least expensive mode of travel in 1846. No passenger lists were required of steamboat or canal boat operators or railroads. My grandmother Carrie's history skipped New York. In fact, before finding the *Sultan* manifest, I was sure my family had sailed directly to Canada. But here they are in New York, on their own. As am I in my story telling. But we can't leave them stranded in New York City. I shift to best-guess mode. I'm going with the typical Norwegian immigration pathway.

****

Finally their trunks and barrels, kegs and parcels were piled around them. Time to hire a cart or wagon to carry their baggage across town to the Hudson River. Did they walk down Coffeehouse Slip road, continue on Wall Street to pass by Trinity Church? The distance from the East River ocean ship docks to the Hudson River steamboat landings is about a mile. What a mile for these Norwegian country folk. Whether they loved it or hated it, it was crowded, dirty, magnificent New York.

The debris mixed with puddles of unknown origin forced Ellen, Marte, Berthe, Kirstin and Nella to hoist their skirts and watch their step. Hurrying along, they might have managed a fast transfer to an evening steamboat and continued their journey, arriving in Troy the next morning. Did they? Or was a layover of a few days more tempting, giving them time to adjust to solid earth under their feet? Forty to fifty ships sailed the Hudson every day, half at 7 a.m., half at 7 p.m., each one as crowded as the next. A day or two of rest wouldn't make much difference.

But soon they were off. The ship was chosen, the departure date set. The steamship owners, Cornelius Vanderbilt among them, were cutthroat competitors, resulting in fare variances from twenty-five cents to several dollars. The transport of luggage was charged separately by weight. The comfort of a berth or stateroom added a few more dollars. The 150-mile trip up the Hudson to Troy, just above Albany, was advertised as a quick 7 to 10-hour journey. Letters from that time, however, report passages of several days. Alternatively, steamboat captains from rival companies occasionally staged an impromptu speed competition on a run up or down the river, blown-up boilers and rammed steamboats a regular result of the game. Passengers were along for the ride.

I imagine the family up early on the day of departure from New York — boarding their steamboat in full daylight to see their new country. Staying together was a feat on those frenetic Hudson River docks, as crowded and frantic as their sister docks on the East River. Immigrants streamed from all directions, all straining to be first on the boat, steamship crews hurrying everyone aboard, promising they were headed for the boat

shown on their baggage-claim ticket. Steam poured out of funnels, all boats ready to go. Each captain aiming to be the first to leave the docks, beating their competitors off the line. Passengers scrambled for a seat, stuffing their carry-on bundles where they could. Perhaps a little food, left over from the ocean crossing, a fiddle, a Bible, and a hand-carved ball and cup for Halvor.

They were aboard.

The island of Manhattan passed by in a haze of steam bellowing from multiple funnels, but by the time the Palisade bluffs came into view, the frenzy had quieted, passengers settled in their seats on deck or below. Ellen gasped at the sight of the Palisades. The family, following her gaze, stared in wonder at the scene; at the bluffs that looked exactly like those standing tall above Rogn beach in Bamble, the beach of their summers, just a short walk from their farms.

Tallak and his fellow loggers and farmers might despair at the rocky hills rising from the shore at the beginning of their journey. But as the river widened from one mile to three, the valley around them opened out and there was the black dirt, the rolling hills, forests thick and broken only by the small settlements along the river's edge. The land began to look less like the rocky fields they had left behind in Norway, and more like the open space they were promised.

****

The Hudson is a beautiful river today. Lined with birches and cedars and dogwood. Sumac. Aspens. Black Locust. Pine trees, species after species. Environmentalists are bringing back the banks and waters fouled by the advance of civilization. Bringing it back to the river that my ancestors traveled in 1846. And yet the steamboat carrying my ancestors up the river, and the millions of Europeans who took this journey after them, began that fouling. The productivity of those millions settled in the Midwest demanded the shipping of millions of tons of produce and grain by canal and river to New York. These innocent advances in civilization began the accumulation of debris lining the banks of the Hudson, and the waste sullying its waters.

There is no record of this particular journey up the Hudson. It might have been a peaceful passage once they got used to the throbbing engines, the constant smoke streaming from the funnel, the occasional battles of steamboats through a narrow channel. A somewhat dreamy view of the land they had left home and heritage to conquer. To work. To civilize.

The journey came to an end with a clatter, another cacophony of activity, finding a spot for the boat to dock, ropes thrown, expletives exchanged, a clang and a jerk and quiet. The Hudson River journey was completed.

The crew prodded the passengers to move quickly, everybody grabbed their bundles and clattered down the ramp to the dock. The young ones scurried, Marte urged her feet to move safely, holding on to the railing, clearly wearying of this constant travel.

Her children followed and the group gathered together on yet another dock. Their baggage was soon beside them, another transfer to manage. There, just across and down the dock, they spied a long, narrow, mast-less, flat-topped boat tied to the cleat. Two mules grazing along the path on the right. They stared at the canal boat and its power sources. The journey continued.

Chapter 8 — 1846 – The Erie Canal

I hope Tallak and Elias had heard some tales of this leg of the journey. There were many distinctions between one choice and another — and so many choices.

They could transfer directly to a canal boat and endure the twenty-seven locks in the thirty miles to Schenectady. Or they could avoid that tedious route with a short rail ride to Schenectady, and board the canal boat there. Most Norwegian immigrants chose that route. Railroad all the way to Buffalo was advertised, but the railroads and tracks were still primitive. The rails of the time were made of wood covered with strap iron; the cars were converted stage coach bodies. Occasionally one of those rail straps would come loose, pierce the wooden floor of the passenger coach, and cut through whatever or whomever it encountered in the coach.

Best guess? The short rail ride to Schenectady and canal boat. Wait — there were two types of canal boat.

Packet boats were first class. Designed to carry sixty to seventy passengers, these boats had priority at the locks, traveled about four miles an hour, and cost $14.52 with *meals*.

Line boats were not first class. They hauled livestock and crops from the Midwest. On the return trip they hauled immigrants. They were dirty, crowded and slower by two miles an hour, and cost around $9.00 with meals. Most immigrants chose the Line boat. Six days to Buffalo, stated the Erie Canal ads.

Gutthorm R. Thistle described a line boat in a letter written in 1844:

> *We neither had room to sit down nor stand up. We felt like so many pigs stowed together. . . [But]we had such fine weather that we could walk on the banks of*

*the canal alongside the boat; we gathered much fruit,
especially apples, and brought it on board the boat in
big sacks. . . .*

Thomas Woodcock, traveling on a packet boat in 1836,
described the large open cabin, with settees along the wall by
day, then at dinner a table was lowered from the ceiling to fill
the open space between the settees for serving the meal. For
nighttime, each settee was folded down to form a bed. Above
them, frames with sacking bottoms and pins to fit into sockets
on one side and cords attached on the opposite corner were
suspended from hooks in the ceiling. *It looked like a bunch of
shelves with bedding with space between for a person to barely
crawl in,* said Woodcock.

H.R. Holland, an early Erie Canal traveler, described his
journey in 1839:

> *"twenty four hours a day of constant commotion"*
> . . . *"incessant and simply maddening racket in
> getting through the locks. . . of loading and unloading
> at the frequent stopping places, the thundering
> collisions with other canal boats, the wrangling and
> foul talk between commanders of the different barges,
> and the awful turmoil and confusion when the whole
> ark, as often happened, ran aground on a mudbank.*

A seat on the deck kept you in the action. But the captain's
shout of "bridge" or "very low bridge" triggered a mad dash to
clear the deck, bend double if seated, or lie down flat on deck.
This was true for both packet and line boats. The bridges were
notorious for knocking off hats and occasionally causing serious
accidents. Fifty years later, Thomas S. Allen's song *Low Bridge,
Everybody Down,* celebrated these bridges and one hundred
years of Erie Canal travel.

The fastest speed allowed was four miles an hour, and this
only possible with the packet boats. Ellen had time to hop onto
a bridge with Halvor, walk the canal path to the next bridge, and

toss Halvor down to Jens before lowering herself onto the deck. What happened if one missed the boat on one of these leisurely walks between bridges? Maybe Berthe, Elias's disappearing spouse, simply missed the boat, was rescued by another prince, married and slid away from my history and into another's. It could be so.

The eighty-three locks of the Erie Canal raised the water 568 feet between the Hudson River and the Lake Erie in 363 miles. Captain, helmsman, bowman, cook and driver comprised the official crew. Family-owned boats were manned by the mother and father and the children. The horses or mules were relieved every four hours or after twelve to fifteen miles. The onshore crew unhitched the tired animals and walked them to a small barn, then hitched up the fresh team. On a family owned boat, the horses or mules traveled with the family and passengers in their on-board stalls. One of the family crew led the rested animals off the boat and coaxed the exhausted beasts up the ramp and into their boat-stall.

My Norwegian newcomers had time to check out the towns along the way, the once sleepy villages transformed to major town status, able to ship and receive merchandise from New York and Chicago. Transport costs were cut by ninety-five percent when the canal replaced shipping by pack animal. The salt of Syracuse could now be found on general store shelves in Wisconsin. The grocery stores and taverns edging the canals offered buying opportunities for the Halverson-Høen family, too. Fresh bread and butter, some apples or fruit, maybe a glass or two to ease the way.

****

My sister Jeanne and I explored Troy in 2015, then followed the New York State highways paralleling the canal. In the year 2000, New York created the Canalway National Heritage Corridor, replacing the old towpaths with bike paths and walking trails, and creating miles of canal, river and lake waterways for recreational boating.

We tromped through overgrown ruins, old towpaths and lock remnants, then explored the still-working locks and canals. The most impressive locks, still existing today, are the Lockport stair steps: five locks rising to the Niagara Escarpment and completing the uphill journey to the level of Lake Erie. In Rochester, a tour on a reproduced canal boat treats tourists with a trip through the locks and down the canal.

****

Sixteen miles after the spectacular Lockport locks, the canal ended in Tonawanda, just above Buffalo, New York. Most immigrants continued their journey on Lake Erie by sail or steamboat, often to a memorized address in a small town in Wisconsin or in Chicago where an earlier immigrating family or friend awaited to welcome these newcomers to America. Tallak and Ellen must have known that most of those Norwegians who sailed on the Sultan with them were headed to Port Ulio, Wisconsin. I suspect that was their destination also.

An unknown resident of Buffalo described the immigrant ship scene as he observed it in 1832:

> *Several steamboats and vessels daily depart for the far west, literally crammed with masses of living beings to people those regions. Some days, near a thousand thus depart. ...I have stood upon the wharves and seen the departure of these floating taverns, with their decks piled up in huge heaps with furniture and chattels of all descriptions, and even hoisted up and hung on to the rigging; while the whole upper deck, and benches, and railing, sustained a mass of human bodies clustering all over them like a swarming hive...*

"A swarming hive?" Hyperbole, I suspect. Let's hope it was more organized in 1846.

My best guess: The family boarded a ship headed to Port Ulio, Wisconsin, twenty-five miles north of Milwaukee.

But detour ahead.

Chapter 9 — 1846 – Detour Canada

My grandmother was succinct.

> *The first place where they stopped was in Canada.
> There Tellif Haines was born in 1848 and there Nellie*
> [Nella] *Halvorsen married a Yankee by the name of
> Chase. They had four children (Eli, Charles, Oscar,
> and Helena).* (Carrie, *History*)

Another writer, Hjalmer Holand, wrote an article about my
great-grandfather published in 1923. He had even fewer words:

> *Tallak Haines was born in 1812, came to America
> in 1848, after having spent a couple of years in
> Canada.*

That's all from Hjalmer. I will tell you more about him in a
later chapter.

I had interpreted these cryptic reports as evidence that the
family had sailed from Norway to Canada, as many Norwegians
did. After searching Canadian records for years, I discovered the
Naeseth Biographical Directory of Norwegian Immigrants,
listing each ship and its manifest that carried Norwegian
emigrants to America between 1825 and 1850. The entire family
was listed, and their Bamble neighbors, sailing on the *Sultan* to
New York City in 1846.

In a sharing moment on one of my visits to Sturgeon Bay,
Wisconsin, my genealogist cousin (more of her expert
contributions coming up) shared a letter she had received from
the granddaughter of Nellie [Nella] Halverson, Ellen's sister.
Margaret Chase Gibson told the story of her grandmother Nella
and how she happened to be in Canada.

Ms. Gibson's story begins:

*They left Langesund Norge, May 12, 1848 [sic]
and did not reach New York until August. They sailed
up the Hudson River to the Erie Canal, thence to the
Welland Canal at Pt. Dalhousie. From there their
journey took them to Lake Erie. At Port Stanley, the
Captain, fearing winter on the upper lakes, since it
was now October, said he had to scrape the ship free
of barnacles. Whether or not Nella came with one or
two brothers, it is certain she came with her younger
brother Ole.*

Port Stanley, Elgin County, Ontario is on the north shore of
Lake Erie, about 130 miles west of Buffalo. The date of May 12
corroborates our research; the year of 1848 contradicts. The
Welland Canal is another deviation from my assumed route.

Ms. Gibson continues:

*Isaac Chase and his Uncle Samuel Haight of the
Union Rd., Sparta had brought a load of grain to Pt.
Stanley for shipping. When Isaac saw Nella he
persuaded Uncle Sammy to talk to the Captain. He
wanted Uncle Sammy to invite the Emigrants to come
to his home, but Uncle Sammy said, "Isaac, hadn't
thee better ask thy Father first."*

*The next day Abner, Isaac's father, drove the ten
miles to Pt. Stanley, talked to the Captain and offered
the shelter of the Haight home to the travelers. Nella,
with her painted wooden trunk, her spinning wheel
and her Lutheran prayer books and her brother (or
brothers) stayed until spring and in May, she and
Isaac were married.*

Nella must have looked terrific coming off that barnacle
covered boat.

But where are the rest of the family? It would be unusual for
Nella, nineteen, and Ole, sixteen, to separate from the family —
they were Marte's youngest.

Did the several plurals ("Emigrants," "travelers") imply that all ten of the family was housed? And what about the other passengers on the barnacle-covered ship? They too needed food and shelter, a place to store their belongings, some comfort at this sudden turn of events. Removing barnacles was a lengthy procedure; by the time that job was done it would be too far into winter to continue on through the Great Lakes. Did this dismissing captain refund their money?

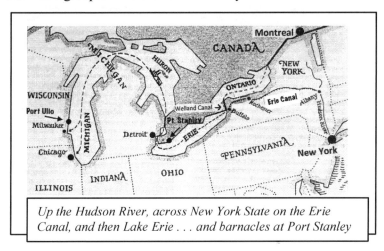

Up the Hudson River, across New York State on the Erie Canal, and then Lake Erie . . . and barnacles at Port Stanley

There was lodging nearby — the Sparta Hotel and various boarding houses between Port Stanley and Sparta. Perhaps most of the passengers found shelter there. The other families in the area might also take in a few of these stranded passengers for the winter.

Margaret Chase Gibson did not respond to early thank-yous for this information, and the window for asking more questions closed in 2010. Ms. Gibson died at age 105; in her long life she had been a school teacher, a volunteer in the Royal Canadian Air Force during WWII and an active member of the Grimsby Historical Society. I would have loved to talk with her.

Mysteries. My search continues today, but in my 2014 visit to Port Stanley and Sparta, I found no evidence of a barnacle-ridden ship landing in Port Stanley and abandoning its passengers on a cold day in 1846 (or 1848) at the Port Stanley dock. I found no evidence of Tallak or any of the other members of the family. But Nella and Isaac had left their mark on the Quaker town of Sparta. Isaac had built a two-story cobble-stone home in Sparta in 1872, and it remained a local tourist attraction in 2014.

Following the tourist guidebook on a cold, dark, rainy afternoon, my sister Jeanne and I found the cobble-stone house right across the street from the Sparta Friends Meeting House. A later tramp through the sopping wet grass of the nearby Friends Cemetery revealed the gravestones of Isaac and Nella, next to the stones of Isaac's parents, Abner and Lydia.

Even though my Norwegian great-great-aunt Nella was buried in the Quaker cemetery, she never became a Quaker, wrote her granddaughter. The marriage certificate of Isaac and Nella, dated May 1849, is signed by a Wesleyan Methodist minister. Nella and Isaac were married "outside the meeting" because Nella was not a Quaker.

Ms. Gibson ends her story thus:

> *Nella never joined the Quaker Meeting . . . a friend of Nella's used to tell us that Nella got a new bonnet and went to Meeting ready to state her wish to join. On her way in to the Women's side she met a Mrs. Pound who said, "Nelly, does thee think thee should wear a rose in thy bonnet?"*
>
> *Nella said, "If thy Lord does not like the rose in my bonnet, he will not like me!" And she never stated her intention of joining. She died a Lutheran.*

****

In any version of the tale, the late landing in Port Stanley in October suggests some delay or detour along the way. They landed in New York in mid-August anticipating a remaining journey of two to three weeks, yet it appeared to take two months. There were plenty of opportunities for delay — transfers from ocean to river to canal to Lake Erie, dangers unlimited with steamboats running aground, boilers blowing up; canal boats jammed up in narrow canals, and sickness or injury to one or two of the ten traveling together.

Or perhaps there is another version of the story placing the whole family somewhere else in Canada for two years, heading north from Tonawanda and taking an early ride on Maid of the Mist ferry, launched in 1846. Then two years of adventure somewhere in Canada, then Nella and Ole were separated from the family and traveled alone on that barnacle crusted ship. That would explain the delayed Lake Erie sailing in October and 1848 date of arrival in Port Stanley.

It's an exciting story. I just don't know it.

****

The Port Stanley area would be a good place for the family to land for a few years. Sparta housed two blacksmiths, three shoemakers, a tailor, harness and saddle maker, scythe manufacturer and a physician/dentist. A printing shop, run by the editor of the True Teller, was close by.

The saw mill and chair factory assured employment for good lumbermen. Tallak and all the men in the family were that — and probably found logging jobs through the winter. Kirsten and Nella might work as hired girls, and in the spring this prosperous farmland would provide multiple farmhand jobs for the men.

Just about the time that ships began sailing the Great Lakes in the spring of 1847, Ellen suggested that they not leave quite yet — she wasn't feeling well enough to travel, a mid-19th century euphemism for "I'm pregnant." The family acquiesced, or perhaps stayed for any number of other reasons — even Ellen knew that her sex encountered much tougher hurdles than a pregnant sail through the Great Lakes. On a Tuesday night in December, somewhere in Ontario, Canada, Ellen developed a headache, and the next morning, December 8, Tellif Tallaksen, her second son, was sleeping peacefully in the cradle. That's just how things happened in 1847.

Wherever and whenever our family traveled, that stop for a barnacle cleaning in October might have been a life saver. Records of Great Lakes shipwrecks in 1846 include:

September: Two propellers wrecked.

October: Four schooners wrecked, sunk, or stranded ashore.

November: A terrible gale with sixteen bodies found and over twenty ships wrecked or run ashore.

Storms, running aground, colliding with sister ships, exploding steamboat boilers, malfunctioning machinery, it is astonishing to read of the number of incidents.

Travel was hell.

****

Nonetheless, sometime in 1848 Tallak and Ellen, mother Marte, Kirsten and Jens and Elias, possibly Berthe, were ready to go on to Wisconsin. Ole went his separate way to settle in Port Huron, Michigan.

Did they consider settling in Canada? Another land of opportunity, a welcoming government and Nella's relationship with Isaac and his family added ties to a respected family in an established community.

But Tallak and Ellen, with Marte and her children, had not forgotten their goal to become Americans. An Extract from the Canadian Immigration Report of 1853 revealed that of the five thousand Norwegian immigrants sailing to Canada in the previous season, only two hundred were lured to stay in Canada. The Høens and Halversens weren't alone in their dream.

They were done with this detour. Time to join their Bamble neighbors who had sailed with them on the *Sultan*. Time to pack up and continue the journey to Port Ulio.

Chapter 10 — 1848 – Wisconsin

The packing and provisioning began again. Summer gardens and fields were harvested, the larder, cellar and barn were fully stocked. Tallak and Elias brought out the barrels and kegs they had stored and refilled them with the dried or salted meat and fish, canned, dried and pickled fruit and vegetables, not for the journey this time, but for the winter ahead in Wisconsin. After two years of living in Canada, Ellen dragged the trunks from storage and tucked away the household goods, farm tools, linens and clothing.

> *. . From Canada the others moved to Port Washington, Wisconsin and to a little place called Port Ulio. There Ellen's mother died and was buried, but they can't find the place any more.* (Carrie, *History*)

The date of the move is suggested by deeds for Port Ulio land found in Tallak's name in October of 1848. Sometime after the harvests of that year, the family left Canada for the shores of Lake Michigan in the state of Wisconsin.

Nella would marry Isaac in May of the following year and surely she was engaged by the time her family decided to continue their journey to Wisconsin. It must have been hard for Marte to leave another daughter behind, even if this one was twenty-one. But Marte might be comforted, knowing that Nella was marrying into a prosperous family.

Steamboats stopped regularly at the Port Stanley dock on the Great Lakes route between Buffalo and Chicago. This busy port depended on its fortunate location for cost effective freight deliveries and shipment, receiving seventy-five stoves and fifty-five tons of plaster one day and shipping wheat, flour and hides to Chicago the next. Tallak and family and the Halversens booked passage on one of these regular arrivals.

Their ticket cost depended on their choice of cabin passage or deck passage. Cabin passengers were assigned a stateroom with bed and bureau and possibly a washstand and basin in the room. It included meals in the dining room and access to the Grand Saloon, often a sumptuous space extending the length of the ship, furnished with plush velvet settees, gold-trimmed mirrors, game tables and even a piano for evening sing-a-longs.

Deck passengers provided their own bedding and food, and slept and dined on deck. They could rent a stove to cook their food, but the deck was often too crowded to cook. Meals could be purchased for twenty-five cents. Whether the ship was going east or west, the decks were often already crowded with the passengers who boarded in Chicago or Buffalo.

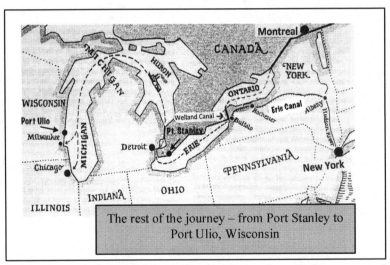

The rest of the journey – from Port Stanley to Port Ulio, Wisconsin

Small children could be trampled in such a setting — surely the matriarch Marte, and Tallak and Ellen and their babies could afford cabin passage. The younger folks might enjoy a deck-full of sleep mates.

Tallak and Ellen, carrying baby Tellif and holding Halvor's hand, Marte, Elias, Kirsten, and Jens, and maybe Berthe, boarded one more boat. Ole may have travelled with his family as far as Port Huron, Michigan. The rest of the family went on their way to Wisconsin.

They sailed the length of Lake Erie to Detroit, then north on the St. Clair river to Lake Huron, and finally around Mackinac Island into northern Lake Michigan. An early traveler declared that here, just rounding Mackinac Island, was the view that revealed the true vastness of the West. Tallak peered at the acres and acres of timber, his hands tingling, anxious to heft the axe once again. Ellen gloried too in the beauty and riches of this new land.

Ellen kept a close eye on four-year-old Halvor. He swaggered a bit, this tiny yet experienced traveler. Tellif at ten months might have tried out his immature legs on the deck, but preferred Ellen's or Tallak's arms for most of the trip. Or his grandmother Marte's. Aunt Kirsten, Uncle Elias and Jens were probably perfectly acceptable too — this family had been traveling together for a long time. It was quite fortunate to be the baby in this close extended family.

They traveled 623 miles. The steamship used six hundred cords of wood. It took the trees from ten or more acres of land to produce that wood. A one month count of the ships plying the Great Lakes in July 1846 revealed two types of steamboats, seventy-one driven by paddlewheels and one hundred thirty-seven driven by propellers, and two types of sailing vessels, fifty-nine brigs, and one hundred-twenty-eight schooners. Sailing vessels, requiring only the wind for power, still outnumbered steam-powered ships, but that ratio would soon reverse, requiring more wood, more woodsmen. Tallak, and lumberjacks like him, were needed in this wood-dependent world.

The pier of Port Ulio appeared, its docks loaded with wood for the ship's hungry boilers. Mr. James Gifford, the entrepreneur who had plotted the settlement of Port Ulio, had built the pier and the sawmill a few years before. Produce and other wood products were visible too, ready for shipment to Chicago. Tallak pointed to the sawmill on the beach, and the log chute to carry the logs down from the bluff. The passengers craned their necks to see the clearing on the bluff with logs stacked ten high, and loggers shoving the logs into the chute. Around the clearing, however, still standing, were trees, waiting.

Oak, maple, birch, beech, elm, hickory, basswood, butternut, poplar, ash, sumac, alders, willows. Creeping water-vines, tamarack and cedar scattered among them. Bushes of treats of wild grapes, raspberries and blackberries. All decorating the bluffs with their bounty — a blur of green mixed with traces of the gold and red of early fall.

Down the gangplank strode Tallak, confident and eager to explore this abundant landscape, Elias and Jens as eager as their brother-in-law. Berthe's sister, Karen, might be in the welcoming crowd waiting on the dock, scanning that gangplank for her sister, Berthe. Was she there?

Ellen towed Halvor and hugged Tellif to her hip, Marte peered ahead at the crowd of people on shore, willing a glimpse of a familiar face, a Bamble neighbor, a friend from the *Sultan*. Kirsten trailed behind — scanning the crowd for Soren? They would marry within a year or so — it's likely they had become more than neighbor and shipmate on the long voyage on the *Sultan*. The voices traveled toward them, the rhythm of their language embraced them. Velkommen, they heard. Velkommen!

The Port Ulio locals slapped their backs and shook their hands and offered them lodging, happy to see more Norwegians in this polyglot settlement, with Germans, Irish and Belgians already outnumbering the Norwegians.

Port Ulio, the smallest of a cluster of four settlements, Port Washington to the north, Grafton to the west, and Saukville northeast, was located twenty-five miles north of Milwaukee. The first Norwegian immigrants had settled in the area in 1844, seven families from a parish just south of Bamble. Those earlier arrivals had landed in the Wisconsin Territory. Tallak and Ellen were stepping onto the soil of the State of Wisconsin in the United States of America. Statehood had arrived in 1848.

Marte, not as impressed with adventure and novelty as her children, reveled in the smiles, the manners, the blondness, the aromas and sensibilities of her countrymen. Halvor and Tellif suddenly had aunts and grandmothers galore. All were welcomed into the community of their old neighbors. Berthe's sister and her family had settled here earlier and Kirsten's friend Soren had also found a place. The hospitality of their neighbors, new and old, gave the family some time to rest, explore, and decide where to build their first home in America. Tallak spent his days getting advice from the earlier settlers and riding through the settlement to find the best deals. Ellen and Kirsten and their mother Marte got to know their neighbors, and asked around about a church.

****

I found them . . . sitting in the 1850 congregational meeting, fourth page, no mistake. The spelling is fuzzy, *Tallag Tellefsen, 38, Elen K.H., 32, Halvor, 6, Tellef, 3, and Melvin, 1.* A few lines below Kirsten, her husband Soren and their firstborn appeared on the list. Below that were Halvor and Karen Anderson, with their two children, Anne Elise, 5, and Berthe Marie, 2. Each entry revealed the name, age, and the Norwegian parish they traveled from; twenty-four were from Bamble, most of them had sailed on the *Sultan* with Tallak and Ellen. All 102 were from Norway, except those recently born in the Holden parish, and most were young couples and their babies. What a discovery in the first half hour in this tiny museum-library, this offbeat lakeshore town.

I had walked into the Port Washington Historical Society at 1 p.m. that Friday in August 2014. Not looking for anything in particular but curious about the vanished settlement of Port Ulio and Marte's gravesite that no one could find. Within minutes of

61

citing my question to the volunteers, I had in my hand the neatly handwritten record of the first meeting of the Holden Evangelical Lutheran Congregation in Port Washington, WI, established January 1850.

The volunteers kept bringing me documents, describing a vibrant 1850 Port Ulio, the history of the church, a description of services held in settlers' homes in Port Ulio and Saukville as well as Port Washington, and yes, the directions to the two Norwegian cemeteries where my 2nd great grandmother Marte might be buried. I looked, but like my grandmother and aunts and uncles and cousins, had no luck in finding the gravesite of Marte or Berthe. Nonetheless, the Port Washington Historical Society will reign as my favorite ever historical research site.

****

My grandmother's history has no word of Berthe and there are no official records of what befell Berthe Marie Hendriksdatter Halverson. But it is probably not coincidental that her sister, Karen Hendriksdatter Anderson, who had sailed on the *Sultan* with her husband and first baby along with Berthe and Elias, had named her second daughter Berthe Marie, born on October 16, 1848 according to the Holden Norwegian Lutheran Church baptism records. It is likely that Elias, arriving in Port Ulio shortly before Karen's child was born, brought the sad news of Berthe's demise, and Karen respectfully fulfilled the Norwegian tradition of naming her daughter after her deceased sister. Karen's choice of name for her baby girl convinces me that Berthe died sometime between arriving in New York and the journey to Port Ulio.

Chapter 11 — 1848 – Property Revelations

I almost missed the clues of property ownership in this first American settlement of my ancestors. I had envisioned my pioneer family as travel-weary, haggard, and if not penniless, certainly impoverished, looking for land to squat on in the woods outside of Port Ulio where the land was cheaper. I had read of the hospitality shown to new immigrants by their earlier emigrating countrymen, but I was sure those first years would be tough. At most, I anticipated one or two deeds to check out.

Finally, in 2016, I decided to take a quick look at the Ozaukee County Register of Deeds and allotted a few hours late in the day on a Friday. I had done weeks of deed research in other counties; I knew the drill. I began with the earliest (1847) index, checking the H's for Høen and Haines and Halverson lookalikes. The results were quick and staggering. There was Tollick Haynes in 1850. Tallec Hayne, 1851; then Tallak selling to Elias, Elias to James, twenty and forty acres for $1, then Talleg Hoen and Henn, and Hann, 1852. My great-grandfather was buying and selling land from the moment he arrived in America.

I moved to the deed volumes, slower work — I soon realized I had missed something — Tallak was selling property I had no record of his buying. There had to be an earlier deed. But the clerks were turning out the lights. It was 5 p.m.. . . Friday.

Luckily, I had time a week later to complete the job. Voila! Tallak had used his original Norwegian name, Tellefsen, instead of his farm name for his first transaction in October 1848. Tallak Tellefsen bought eighty acres, then added adjacent land in two-hundred acre chunks. By 1850, Tallak owned four hundred eight acres — total cost $950. This land was not out in the woods, in fact it was in the midsection of Port Ulio — close to Lake Michigan and the pier. More deeds in 1853-4, both buying and now selling portions of the original purchases. Portions cleared of salable lumber, no doubt.

The fact that Tallak bought parcels in two separate sections of Port Ulio, and then transferred the smaller of the parcels (forty acres) to Elias and James for one dollar, suggests that he was the appointed property acquisition agent for the entire family. When the two brothers-in-law left the area, they sold their land for a profit in their own names. It didn't revert to Tallak.

The transactions, both buying and selling, were cash and credit. Tallak paid his mortgages back on time and sometimes foreclosed on a buyer. His final sale of seventy-seven acres of land was completed ten years after he had left the area. Sale price? Two thousand dollars.

****

The unique spellings of the names of my ancestors found in the early documents need some explanation. It's a simple formula: The surname of a child is composed of the first name of his or her father plus "son" or "sen" for a male, "datter" for a female. Tallak's Norwegian surname was Tellifsen after his father Tellif Anundsen, whose father was Anund. Ellen, whose father was Halvor, was named Ellen Halvorsdatter. To complicate, it was customary for owners or even workers to take the name of the farm as surname. When Tallak purchased the Høen farm, he took the name Tallak Tellifsen Høen.

The Norwegian naming system generates many identical surnames; that, added to the tradition of giving each child the first name of a specific grandparent or aunt or uncle, leaves parish and census records with page after page of identical first and last names. Finally, few rural citizens could write. They spoke the dialect of their area, a language not written down until 1850, when the language of *nynorsk* was created from multiple rural dialects. *Bokmål*, a combination of Danish and Norwegian, was and still is the language of business, the church, and the urban citizenry. The name bestowed on a child at his birth was spoken by the family, a parish priest wrote what he heard and spelled it his way. The family knew no written name.

America was no different. Ellen and Tallak spoke their name to the record-keeper, who wrote what he heard and spelled it however he pleased. Nineteenth century newspapers continued the tradition of translating the sound into letters that appealed to them that day. It didn't help that Tallak alternated his several surnames in the early years in America. He calls himself Tallak Tellifsen on the ship's manifest, in the 1850 Port Ulio Lutheran parish register and in early deeds, followed by variations including Hayes, Hayne, Hoen, Henn, Hann, Hain, Haine and multiple Tallak lookalikes on deeds, census records and newspaper accounts. The Haines name stuck about 1875. Tallak stabilized as Tallack on his headstone.

In this manuscript, I settled on a spelling for each name using the version I saw most often in the earliest days. Thus came "Tallak," "Ellen," "Jens," "Tellif," and some of the other more variably spelled names. I use my version whenever I refer to these individuals in my own words; however, when quoted I use the name used by the source. "Tellif" is one of the most difficult —— it is so close to "Tallak" that I confuse them myself.

Ellen and her sisters lost both their first and last names in America, as they melted into the pot of American women called Mrs. Surname-of-husband.

Tallak's signature stayed the same throughout his life: "X."

****

Tallak began his land dealings in Port Ulio, challenging my assumptions of impoverished immigrant ancestors. But money in his pocket when the family arrived in America doesn't negate the threat of starvation in Norway. The years of harvests inadequate to last through the winters happened to the entire community. No food at this farm meant no food at the neighboring farm. It meant no food at the market. Cash in your pocket was useless and most had none — their assets were farms and property. Because both Marte and Tallak owned their farms, the sale turned their assets into cash, silver speciedallers. Nonetheless, the Port Ulio deeds inform my story and my perceptions. A family of means. Not the idle rich, but financially secure from their labors.

And Tallak's wits, perhaps?

Chapter 12 — 1849 – Port Ulio.

The family stuck together in the early days of Port Ulio. Finding a place of shelter for all the family was top priority. If they were staying with settlers who had come before them, they were probably split up — there were still seven of them, including baby Tellif, and Halvor, the four-year-old. Most settlers' homes were around twelve by fourteen feet, most one room, some with a loft. Tight. Sharing with another family — Super Tight.

One of the first properties Tallak purchased had a home already built on the 280 acres. That fact was mentioned in the deed only because the seller kept the right to continue to live in the house for a year. It wasn't customary to mention the detail of a house in the deed — sometimes the word "appurtenances" showed up in the description but it could mean a barn or shed, crops or plowed fields, or simply real estate boilerplate. But if one of the Port Ulio parcels had a house, maybe another of Tallak's purchases did too. Starting out with a ready-made shelter would be ideal for a while, and get the family back together again. For a little longer, at least.

They cleared the land, for garden, fields, outbuildings, and for a larger home as the family grew. There would be trees on that 280 acres. They would come down.

Beautiful trees, to people of today, as they stood. Beautiful to Tallak in their utility, their necessity for building a home, barn, privy, outbuilding, for fuel to keep family and animals warm, to bake bread and boil stew, for crafting furniture, shelves and cabinets, carving the kitchen spoon and spatula, fabricating fences, wagons and their wheels, buckets, oxen yokes, and toys for the children. The trees needed to get out of the way for gardens, fields of grain, and houses, to allow the sun to beam down to grow the crops and cheer the soul. Ellen probably felt quite the same as Conrad Richter's fictional pioneer woman Sayward in his novel "The Fields":

> *The sweetest sound to a human deep in these woods was the hard whack of the axe, cutting or splitting, trimming or hewing, ringing a long ways through the timber till all the trees around knew what was coming to them.*

Once the homestead needs were met, Tallak, Elias and Jens kept cutting. Their new country craved timber. The market demanded raw material for sailboats, steamboats, railroad cars, ties and trestles and houses for the city slickers who didn't have their own trees. The trees of Port Ulio powered steam engines and iron smelters. This town had the sawmill to make the boards and shingles and the pier to dock the ships and load their holds.

Their first house in America was much the same as those of their Port Ulio neighbors, even if Tallak was still carrying unspent capital. One room with a fireplace for cooking and heating in the corner, narrow beds with mattresses stuffed with straw, grass or sawdust along the wall, curtains between the beds for privacy. A loft would add an ideal space for Halvor and Tellif to escape and to allow a semblance of privacy to Tallak and Ellen in their lower floor bed space. Ellen would appreciate a new wood stove replacing her fireplace cooking hook — as soon as possible, please. Their new land, a mile away from the freight freeway of the Great Lakes, assured a ready source of the latest in technology — wood stoves undoubtedly a hot item.

Move-in day. Time to unpack once again. Ellen, Marte and Kirsten worked together, lifting the linens and quilts, dinnerware and silverware, pots and pans and treasures from the trunks packed carefully in Norway (and re-packed after their stay in Canada). The cradle surfaced, three babies old; Ellen suspected it would be needed soon again. The rocking chair was placed close to the fire, with sewing supplies — scissors, knitting needles, thread, thimble — stored close by. The spinning wheel stood in the corner. That wheel had traveled far, still used to spin wool into yarn to be knit or crocheted into clothing and coverlets for cold winter days. Ready-made fabric, cotton and linen, was available at the general store, but the sewing? Handwork, every stitch. The work of the evening, by the light of the fire.

Tallak and the men spread out the farming and logging and fishing tools, tallied whatever seeds were left. But now these treasures must be shared. Kirsten, soon to be married to Soren, needed those same tools to begin her own household. Elias and Jens would soon need their share too.

In that first year of 1849, Ellen's pregnancy with Melvin, who was born in January of 1850, probably didn't slow her down, at least until fall. When Kirsten married and their mother died, Ellen became the sole mistress of her home for the first time since Norway. Did she enjoy her independence? Her life had been communal for a long time. The burden of this pioneer household could be onerous for just one woman. The chores she knew in Norway resumed in this new country. Add two young boys and another child almost here.

But Christmas was coming, and everyone looked forward to celebrating it here, in Port Ulio, with most of their family still together, and with neighbors and friends accustomed to the Norwegian traditions. Ellen corralled Halvor and Tallak hefted Tellif onto his shoulders on the day before Christmas Eve, only Marte stayed at home as her family braved the cold to search the forest for the very best Christmas tree, a tradition the Norwegians had adopted from Germany in the 1820s. On Christmas Eve Tallak and the men gathered the livestock to spend the night in the shanty — even those who traditionally roamed outdoors throughout the winter had a warm bed on this night.

****

My cousin Don grew up on a farmland first purchased by his great-grandfather Tallak. His father, named Tallack for his grandfather (the final spelling of our great-grandfather's name — the name on his headstone) shared with his son the tradition of adding a forkful of the second-cutting timothy to the feeding trough of each of his cows on Christmas Eve.

****

On this first Christmas in Port Ulio, Ellen helped Halvor gather a bundle of grain to set out for the birds, the *julenek* — the Christmas sheaf.

An early immigrant shares customs in Wisconsin in the 1850s:

> *. . . they had home-brewed ale, made from malt or molasses or sugar cane.... Nearly everybody slaughtered for Christmas so that they could have meat and sausages. Then they had potatoes and flatbrød* (flatbread) *and smultringer* (doughnuts) *and sauce made from dried apples. And most of them had rømmegrøt* (cream porridge)*. We youngsters liked to stay and listen to the old folks and thought it good fun when they told about old things in Norway.*

Everyone joined in the trimming of the tree, Halvor and Tellif crawling or toddling around their feet. Jens popped the corn and even Marte joined in to string the corn and cranberries for draping on the tree. For just this night, candles were clipped to the branches, but no, not lit, not yet. If it was anything like my childhood, the dishes must first be washed and put away. Then the candles could be lit, and Tallak distributed the gifts. Homemade toys, maybe a new cap for Halvor and Tellif — the grown-ups were content to sing a few hymns around the tree. Ale — was there ale for this first Christmas in America? Happy to be in Port Ulio. Happy to be in America.

Church on Christmas Day would have to wait a year until the

Lutheran Church was established. But the Norway tradition of bobsledding from farm to farm on Christmas Day and through the twelve days of Christmas would be joyous in this community of Norwegian Americans, every wife showing off her *smultringer, rømmegrøt* and *smørbrød plate* (sandwich plate).

On the thirteenth day after Christmas Ellen developed that headache and went to bed early. The next morning Melvin was lying in the cradle. Another miracle! The midwife went home, Marte and Kirsten kept Halvor and Tellif occupied and eased the chores for a few days. But women of the day had no time for long recoveries, and Ellen was soon back to her indispensable role in her partnership with Tallak, now with two small boys around her knees, and one at her breast.

Chapter 13 — 1854 –The Siblings Scatter

The family had broken the ties with their native land of Norway and crossed the ocean and half of the United States together. Nella and Ole slipped out of the knot of family in Canada and it is here, in Port Ulio, where the final untying occurs. Mother Marte leaves this earth, her children find their separate futures.

> *There* [Port Ulio] *Ellen's mother died and was buried, but they can't find the place any more. In Port Ulio Kirsten married Soren Anderson. They had three children but only one, Mary Jane, lived.*

> *Elias Halvorsen bought a farm in Manitowoc, married Andrea and they had five children (Alfin, Tella, Mary, Melvin and Berthe). Jens Halvorsen bought a farm in Star Prairie, Minnesota* [Wisconsin], *married and had a big family. . .* (Carrie, *History*)

****

Elias had purchased land from Tallak in August of 1851, but sold it to Jens, or James, as he was already calling himself, a year later. Elias married Andrea in 1853 in Valdres, fifty miles from Port Ulio. Jens disposed of his Port Ulio land in July 1854, and in that same year married and moved to Star Prairie, Wisconsin. Cholera swept the settlement of Port Ulio in the summer of 1849 and again in 1854, when sixty-five deaths occurred in ten days. Marte, whose name never appeared as a member of the Holden Lutheran Church, could have been a victim of one or the other of those cholera outbreaks. Jens and Elias might have been reluctant to leave Port Ulio while their mother was living, and I suspect that Marte was gone before Elias married Andrea.

Kirsten was still in town, but in her own house with her husband Soren, and starting her own family. Tallak and Ellen and their children were home alone. But this independent unit continued to grow. Marie Toilette Kristine was born in April of 1852. The first girl since the death of Gunhild. Ellen's thoughts must have strayed to her firstborn, who had lived just twenty-six days, and now lay in the Bamble Kirke cemetery, so far away.

Tallak and Ellen continued their life in Port Ulio. Halvor, the first-born, helped with the home chores in the early years, but by age seven or eight he was out with his father or uncles learning to hunt, log and fish. About that time Tellif, now five, could take over Halvor's chores at home, and Melvin, well, Melvin could churn the butter and bring in a little firewood. While Ellen's brothers, Elias and Jens remained with the family, it was Ellen who prepared the meals, a little more bread to bake, fruit and vegetables to gather and chop, fish to fry. Tallak, Elias or Jens lugged the fresh kill home from the hunt, elk or deer or moose. The bigger the animal the bigger the butchering job. Ellen set a hunk aside to last a few days, then together the men and Ellen divided the remainder into practical-sized cuts to salt or dry.

Two years after Marie's birth, Eli was born. Halvor, now ten, regularly worked with Tallak. But Ellen had a home crew of Tellif, age seven, Melvin, five, Marie, three, only Eli still a babe in arms. Her team was half helpful and half underfoot. But each handled the chores their hands and heads could manage, each was charged with looking out for the others, each an apprentice in the life of the American frontiersman . . . or woman.

The Port Ulio area too, was growing. The county advertised for new settlers, describing the homes of the current residents as "delightful log cabins, poor outside and elegant within." The steamers and sailing craft arrived in increasing numbers. By 1853 Port Ulio's sister town of Port Washington had 2,500 citizens and 300 dwellings, 10 stores, 5 hotels, 3 mills, 2 breweries, 5 blacksmiths and 4 wagon makers, 6 shoe shops and 5 tailor shops. There were 5 Christian Churches meeting in homes, and the German Catholics had built the first church building. The brick factory and chair factory were close by. The courthouse was built in 1854. The town was exporting cord wood, barrels of wheat and rye flour, bushels of potatoes, tons of saleratus and potash, fish, lumber and hides.

****

"Tons of saleratus and potash." Potash was created by boiling the ashes of burnt trees and, like today, used for fertilizer. But further purifying of potash, through many steps of boiling and fermenting, created saleratus, which was popular as a leavening agent for making bread and biscuits. Saleratus was edged out by baking soda in about 1860.

****

The predominant German culture of the community was increasingly apparent to my Norwegian ancestors. German was the language on the street, in business, and in the public school. According to "Port Washington History" published in 1881, schools had been built in Port Washington as early as 1846 and by 1852 there were five school districts in the area with a total of 535 students. But despite an 1854 national law stipulating English be spoken in the schools, the predominantly German teachers continued to teach their predominantly German students in their common native language. If Halvor and Tellif were given time off from their chores to attend school, their Norwegian parents might whisk them out on the day they came home from school and asked for a snack of "frankfurters" or "strudel."

The early plat of Port Ulio was vacated by the State of Wisconsin in 1856; the piers of Port Washington sufficed for shipments to and from the area, and not as many steamboats stopped "to wood" now that coal was shoveled into those boilers. The Port Ulio sawmill and pier slowly disintegrated. The trees were thinning. Perhaps this town, now called Grafton, was becoming too civilized for Tallak and Ellen. Many of their Norwegian friends had already left for places farther west or north. In the summer of 1855, Tallak and Ellen said their goodbyes to their remaining Norwegian friends and to Kirsten and her family.

Tallak and Ellen, hovering around age forty, and the children, Halvor, Tellif, Melvin, Mary, and Eli, headed north. Ellen's sisters and brothers had chosen to settle in Norwegian settlements with proven farming lands along Lake Michigan and in central Wisconsin. This family was heading toward a land a little wilder, and oddly enough, where few Norwegians had settled.

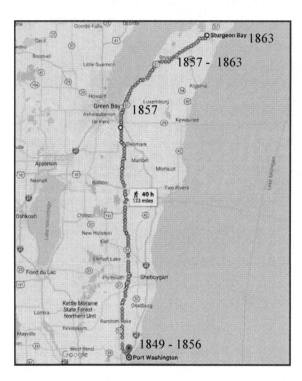

Picture this family of seven leaving home once again, this time on land in their covered wagon, a combination of today's moving van and camping trailer, walking and riding through the forest.

Chapter 14 — 1855 – By Land and Wagon

My grandmother didn't have much to say about this journey.

> *Tallak and Ellen Haines moved on to Green Bay,*
> *lived there for awhile, and then moved to Sugar creek.*
> (Carrie, *History*)

But now we hear from a witness to the journey from Port Ulio to Green Bay. My great aunt Mary, the same Marie Toilette Kristine born in the previous chapter, shared her memories in a 1935 interview with Harry Danker, reporter for the *Door County Advocate*:

> *the family made their way in a covered wagon to Green Bay on the rough trail through the dense forests. They had two Germans to drive the stock. One yoke of oxen were named Buck and Bright, and . . . one of the cows was named "Yulebret."*

Aunt Mary, her family name for all generations, was in her early eighties when she spoke to the reporter, relating events that happened when she was three years old. There may be some fanciful remembering in her stories. Perhaps some fanciful reporting layered on top. Reporters are writers. They have their own motivations and interpretations.

But her reflection suggests that our family had continued to prosper in Port Ulio. The oxen could be raised by Tallak simply by castrating a young bull, then training the bull turned steer to work hard. That's all it took to create an ox. But the presence of two hired men on this journey and the fact that Yulebret was just "one" of the cows, suggests multiple livestock on the trip. Despite their prosperity, their travel accommodations were limited by the amenities of the era.

Mary described the old road as a "dense trail." It had begun as a foot trail cleared by native Americans, the Menominee, Ojibwa, Potawatomi and Ho-Chunk (Winnebago), tribes prominent in Wisconsin when the white man first arrived. Many remained when Tallak and Ellen traveled toward Green Bay, but progressively nefarious government treaties continued to push the tribes further west.

Missionaries and traders shared the trail with the native Americans, then the British and American military widened it to accommodate marching troops, and now in 1855 the earliest immigrants were braving the woods. Tallak and Ellen were on their shortest journey so far — just one hundred miles from Port Ulio to Green Bay — their first journey without extended family, just themselves and their five children and the Germans.

The oxen lumbered along the trail, pulling the wagon loaded with everything Ellen and Tallak had accumulated, both the things they had brought from Norway and those they acquired in Canada and Port Ulio, all packed into a space about four feet wide by twelve feet long. Yulebret and the other livestock plodded along behind. The chicken coop hung off the back.

The roadbed was well-packed from the feet and wagons that had gone before, but their daily comfort was dictated by the weather — the road turned to dust during hot, sunny, spells. Dust that deviled their days, blurred their vision, chafed their faces, seasoned their beans and biscuits. Rain could be worse, ruts became rivers, dust turned to mud; heavy, soppy clothes slowed their actions. Was there room in the wagon to take refuge through a storm?

Wind and storms increased the road maintenance required along the way. Gullies stopped the oxen — out came the shovels to level the way. Debris, tree limbs, or entire trees blocked the way. Half a day could be lost to clearing.

****

The Germans stopped the oxen, then helped Tallak and Halvor clear the trail. A tree had fallen across the road since the last traveler. They had made good time, keeping up a pace of ten miles in a day, but this delay could take an hour. The tree was moved, and Tallak took the opportunity to check the hub and axle — no repairs needed yet. The Germans checked the hooves on the oxen. Overused oxen developed hoof problems, and if they had only one team, that could cause a worse delay of a day or even two. Not all oxen were shod, but if shod, they wore two shoes on each foot, to accommodate their split hooves. An alternative was making a rawhide bag to protect each foot. Since the ox could not hold one foot up for shoeing, pioneer shoeing was done by digging a shallow hole and throwing the ox upside down in the hole; more sophisticated locations used a hoist to lift the ox off the ground for shoeing. I don't know how one throws an ox upside down.

Ellen took advantage of the stop to bring out the midday meal, a little early but they could all use a rest. Oxen traveled at about two miles an hour, even the youngest walkers kept up, but Ellen tired when carrying Eli, and Mary needed a lift once in a while. They gathered for the meal, easing themselves down on the canvas that Halvor laid on the flattest and driest spot he could find. The Germans joined them.

****

Their wagon might be a reinforced farm wagon, or perhaps Tallak built it specifically to the covered wagon specs of the time. Conestoga, prairie schooner, or Mormon style, the canvas tops about the same, first greased to make them waterproof, then stretched over the curved wood bows to make a cover. Their possessions were further protected from rain and dust by pulling the drawstrings at each end to close the canvas cover.

But the image of families perched on the high seat of the

wagon is a myth of the movies; there was seldom a seat at all, just a board jutting out to stand on behind the oxen, sometimes a "jockey box" for storage of small items. This wagon, as most in that era of long overland journeys, was more moving van than camper, with little room and too much bouncing for any comfort. Advice for covered wagon travel included providing a flat space for sleeping by packing household possessions in boxes constructed the same height as the sideboards. But the spinning wheel and butter churn, the cradle and the rocker might be piled high on any smooth surface for this short trip. The lantern hung on a hook attached to the wagon bow, next to the rifle and shotgun, handy to the front opening. Did Tallak have a military model Colt hidden in the jockey box?

Hooks mid-wagon held buckets and bonnets, Mary's rag doll and Melvin's sling shot. Ax and shovel, animal trap and fiddle hung close to the back opening. Flour, coffee, potatoes, beans and corn meal were packed in the makeshift pantry box just inside the back, ready for Ellen to whip into meals. The cow and the chickens provided milk and eggs. Somewhere was stored an extra wagon wheel and a bucket of grease for those axles. The load could equal 2,000 pounds; more than that and the oxen might rebel, the axle crumple. The iron wood stove was left behind.

****

The family walked the hundred miles and slept outside with their quilts and pillows. Ellen was first up, nudging Halvor and Tellif to start the fire and gather the livestock. Tallak took up his shotgun and went ahead on the trail; he might scare up some game, promising fresh meat for evening, or even breakfast, if he was quick enough. Ellen mixed up the biscuit dough, cracked the eggs, sliced the potatoes, and set the iron skillet on the flat rocks that Tellif had placed just so in the fire. The kettle steamed. Coffee mugs appeared. Ellen had learned early in this trip to let the three youngest sleep as long as they would — it speeded things up.

The boys led the oxen to the yoke and the Germans hooked them into their traces. Ellen gathered the dried fish and fruits for the noontime meal, leftover biscuits would fill it out. That midday rest was necessary for oxen, children, parents, and Germans too. Walking ten miles a day was nothing new for Tallak and Ellen, but their boots had to have been well broken in for this trip. They were made of leather on a straight last, with no left or right foot, probably in one of those six shoemaker shops around Port Ulio. Barefoot was the usual mode for the children in summer; for this forest trail they might be wearing smaller replicas of their parents' footwear.

Ten days, maybe a few more, up at dawn, walk till noon, rest, walk till dusk, find the right spot and set up camp all over again. Tallak shouting directions: Halvor, give a hand to the drivers with the oxen, Tellif, fetch the water from that stream. Ellen chimes in: Melvin, pick up some dry kindling, stay close to the camp, Mary and Eli, don't stray — and don't go into the trees. Then supper, prepared over the fire by the expert Ellen, then cleanup and nighttime preparations. Let the fire smoke a bit to keep the mosquitos away. Put the food up high to resist the bears and other predators.

And on the next day, did Tallak and Ellen walk side by side on this first journey with no in-laws, just the two of them, their children around them and in their arms? Did they discuss the day, the trail, tomorrow, their plans and dreams? I don't know.

****

The family rumbled into the city of Green Bay and again found many fellow immigrants. Most were from Germany, but Ireland, Holland and Scandinavia were well represented too. Aunt Mary remembers:

> *. . . when they were in Green Bay she, then 3 1/2 years old, followed some girls and got lost, and was taken in by a negro woman, and after given some food was returned to her parents.* (Danker, *DCA*, 1935)

A cosmopolitan city.

And an old one. The town of Green Bay had the ideal location at the meeting of the Fox River and the waters of Green Bay, that 120-mile-long arm of Lake Michigan. The French discovered the bay in 1634, and built a mission for Indians and fur traders in 1671. The British arrived in 1763 and stayed until the war of 1812. The *Green Bay Intelligencer* began publishing in 1833, and by the time Tallak and Ellen arrived in 1855, the population of Green Bay was over 1,900, a city of mansions built by the British next to log cabins built by the old traders and the recent rush of immigrants.

So, as Grandma Carrie described, they "lived there for a while." Her words, and the fact that Aunt Mary remembers a few incidents about the place, are the only guides for this interval. Maybe they lived in that covered wagon. Some did. They found the Norwegian corner of the city and made friends, worked together for food and shelter. The thriving lumber business of Green Bay might lure Tallak into a logging camp for the winter of 1855-56 to add to their finances. Ellen and the children could get along. Ellen was not the only lumber widow in the Scandinavian community. There was a three-year gap between Ellen's pregnancies in this period of their travel. Could be that logging camp. Could be Ellen demanding a rest.

Chapter 15 — 1856 – By Land and Sea

The Green Bay interval could have been a year or two. The date markers are the two children, Eli, born in Port Ulio on May 20, 1854 and their next child, Christine, born on October 14, 1857 in the place that Grandma Haines and Aunt Mary called Sugar Creek, not a town, just a creek named Sugar.

Some members of the party went by land from Green Bay to Sugar Creek and some in a row-boat, and when [we] neared our destination, [I] saw the breakers and thought it was a fence. (Danker, Interview with Aunt Mary)

Mary was four or five at the time of this move — her memory slightly more trustworthy. It sounded like spring of 1856 when Tallak and Ellen and Halvor, almost twelve, Tellif, Melvin, Mary and Eli and the two Germans started off for Sugar Creek. This trip was the shortest so far — about three days by either land or water. The covered wagon was loaded up once again to cart their worldly goods from Green Bay to their new home. They were headed another twenty-five miles northwards into wooded wilderness.

The family and the Germans split up as assigned to either man the boats or walk the trail. The land crew walked again on a path first blazed by Native Americans, a path followed in 1634 by the French Explorer Jean Nicolet, the first European to discover Lake Michigan and the land that become the State of Wisconsin. Now in 1856 the family traveled the trail wagon-rutted by immigrants before them, wandering north and east along the shore of Green Bay. If the covered wagon and row-boat crews traveled at the same time, they could keep a parallel course, the row-boat crew close enough to the shore to keep an eye on the covered wagon, stopping for meals and camping overnight together.

Aunt Mary continued her Sugar Creek story:

> *[They located] on two forties in the town of Union, and got out logs for the F. B. Gardner sawmill at Little Sturgeon. There was a log scoot at the edge of the cliff and here the logs went down into the water and were then rafted to Little Sturgeon. (Danker)*

The deed to this chunk of Sugar Creek land is written in an elegant, flowing hand, signed by President James Buchanan, land straight from the United States of America to Tallak Hoen of Door County, Wisconsin, according to the Act of Congress on the 24th of April 1820. At a cost of $1.25 per acre Tallak purchased one hundred twenty-two and thirty-six one hundredths acres. Cost: $152.95. Oddly, this deed dated February 22, 1858 was recorded on March 23, 1864 — could it have been a Civil War delay? The deed cites three adjacent forty acre plots, not two as Mary said, a rectangle of land 3/4ths of a mile north to south and one quarter mile east to west, two county roads intersecting at its northwest corner today. The creek called Sugar doesn't touch Tallak's land, but slithers around in the forty to the east.

An earlier Door County deed creates a puzzle. Tallak bought one hundred acres in the Big Creek area of Sturgeon Bay, twenty some miles north of Sugar Creek, from Marcus Bockman a year before the purchase of the Sugar Creek property, but after the family had settled there. Simultaneously Tallak sold seventy-four acres of land in Port Ulio to Marcus Bockman. It appeared almost a trade, except Tallak paid $1,100 for one hundred acres; Bockman paid $2,000 for seventy-four.

Did Tallak consider moving to that Sturgeon Bay land? By the time the Big Creek deed was signed, Ellen was seven months pregnant. Can you imagine Ellen's reaction to the suggestion that they move on to Sturgeon Bay?

Now look here, Tallak. Last year I walked a hundred miles through the deep deep woods, carrying your son Eli in my arms, cooking over a dingy little fire morning noon and night, then I camped out in Green Bay while you took off for lumber camps and rambling, we get here and plow and plant, Eli has finally learned to keep out of the brambles, I just got the curtains hung in the shanty, the crops are close to harvest . . . and now you want me to leave this, pack up, and walk another twenty miles to more wilderness farther north, seven months pregnant and still carrying Eli in my arms? Really, Tallak, you bought that land just to convince Bockman to buy our Port Ulio land. You use it. Go hunt on it. Cut down some trees. I'm here.

That's what Ellen would say.

They were wise to stay in Sugar Creek. The close-by settlement of Little Sturgeon, located on Little Sturgeon Bay in Green Bay (not to be confused with the town of Sturgeon Bay, located on Sturgeon Bay, twenty miles north) had a thriving sawmill, grist mill and general store. The settlement of Little Sturgeon was the oldest and the most prosperous in the county. In contrast, Sturgeon Bay was struggling. The recession of 1857 lasted a year and a half, caused a five thousand- person job loss in the United States, halted the railroad boom and building of all kinds, and slashed the price of lumber for the duration. Consequently, all but three of Sturgeon Bay's many sawmills had failed. Not even a general store had yet appeared in rough and tumble Sturgeon Bay.

They stayed in Sugar Creek. There was a good possibility that Tallak and the older boys had cleared some trees for a garden and home site before this move. Let's give even more luxury to the pregnant mother of five and assume that the house was built and livable when Ellen and the children arrived, the cook stove was in position in the kitchen and the potbellied stove in the center of the large room had warmed things up a bit. Tallak and the boys could do that.

Boxes and barrels were strewn about for an unpacking process familiar to us today. Ellen might have required some carpentering done as she surveyed the number of shelves provided. There would never be enough. But first both Ellen and the men worked together to get the crops planted for the maximum growing season. Once again, laying up food for humans and animals was the priority. Shelves could come later.

Sugar Creek was another step north, another step away from people and deeper into the wilderness. What was the plan? Was it the timber calling? Yes, of course. Tallak was a logger and the trees were there. Ellen knew how to survive, even to thrive, in the wild. But did they want to be loners? How did they find this lovely Sugar Creek land? Had Port Ulio neighbors scouted the land and sent word? Did they have dreams of creating their own Norwegian community? Perhaps there was a glimmer of an idea much grander than cutting down trees.

****

I drove the roads of Sugar Creek, now the town of Union, in August of 2014, found the creek along Ledge Road, almost covered over with the grasses and bushes hanging along its banks. I recognized raspberries, black berries, marion berries; the trees were slim-trunked now; reeds, even pussy-willows, rose up through the clear creek called Sugar, narrow, moving languidly. There were no cars on the road. It was a peaceful scene. The reeds rustled, grasshoppers popped up from the creek, suddenly a blur of soft sounds, movement . . . Ellen? and small children trailing around . . . a field trip, foraging for berries and herbs. Ellen pointed out the leaves to pick, tore a leaf to taste and smell, described the soup or stew it would embellish, the children half-listening, their mouths smeared a bright raspberry red.

Chapter 16 — 1857 – Sugar Creek

Tallak and Ellen and their five children were the first white settlers on this government land. When the British left in 1783, the United States government designated the Door County peninsula as Indian Territory. By treaty of 1831 - 1832 the government "bought" the land from the tribes. Each new treaty revoked the previous, until the tribes lost most of their land in Door County with little recompense. In 1820 villages of Ojibwa [Chippewa], Ottawa and Potawatomi were seen the length of the peninsula; by 1870 there was one Potawatomi village. When Tallak and family arrived in 1857, various tribes still lived in the neighborhood.

The Indians had left the land for these settlers much as they had found it thousands of years before. Northern Europeans, however, had learned a different way of life, and Scandinavians, Germans, Belgians and Irish joined together to make way for their lifestyle. The trees must be cleared. They succeeded in a short seventy years. By 1900 the trees of Wisconsin had been conquered and the logging business declined.

The Scandinavians had the longest logging tradition, and were considered expert lumbermen. Tallak took great pride in his logging skills. He logged in Norway, may have kept the skill up in Canada, and probably spent several winters in logging camps around Port Ulio and Green Bay. In Sugar Creek, he tackled the trees of his own land, beginning with the clearing for the shanty. His sons and the Germans composed his logging crew. Tallak's role was "chopper" or "sawyer," the man who wielded the axe, straight handled, short and heavy with wedge-shaped blade. Or two cutting edges if he had picked up the newer double-bit axe. He chopped a V wedge in the tree, another on the opposite side, same height. Then he chopped on one side until the tree toppled, ideally falling where Tallak intended, doing no damage to the other trees or the crew. Trees didn't always follow the rules, however. The worst rogue fall was the "widow-maker," a felled tree caught in the branches of neighbor tree, with no way to guess where or when it might fall.

Halvor and Tellif claimed the job of "swamper" as they chopped the branches from the felled trees and cleared saplings and small bushes in the path of the oxen and logging chains. Tellif learned his jobs from Halvor, by now an experienced member of the logging team. Tellif was eleven, Halvor, thirteen.

> *They lived in a shanty with three rooms — one for the family, one for the two Germans, and the other for the stock. There was a hollow log some four feet in diameter near their house that was used to shelter the calves and pigs. (Danker, Interview with Aunt Mary)*

Calves and pigs living in the hollow log? Stock sharing the shanty? A substantial shanty, if oxen, sheep, and even cows fit in one room of this three-room dwelling. The livestock boarding-house would be in the middle so the heat of the animals could warm the humans on each side. Mary describes a thriving homestead with oxen to haul logs and pull wagons, pigs, cows and sheep to provide protein, milk and wool.

The sandy soil of Sugar Creek favored oak, aspen and red maple, but ash and the softwoods of pine, cedar, tamarack and poplar were part of the mix. Tall straight trees were selected for the shanty, then each log was cut to the right length and stripped of branches and bark. Notches and saddles were cut into the logs with adze and broadax, then everyone pitched in to hoist the shanty walls log by log. When the walls were raised, Tallak and the Germans cut out the doors and windows. Once the shanty was built, attention shifted to clearing the garden and fields. The trees were in the way and down they came, the young swampers stripping off the branches and Tallak or the Germans cutting the logs into manageable lengths before they were dragged off the site. Crosscut saws would soon replace the hand saw for this chore, but in 1860 it took a powerful bicep and a sturdy hand saw to cut through a mammoth log, sometimes three or four feet in diameter.

The oxen dragged the logs to the chute on the bluff. I suspect the Germans led the oxen, once they had chained the logs, attached the chain to the "slip hook" end of a twelve to fifteen-foot chain, and clipped the "grab hook" to the yoke of the oxen. The oxen preferred dragging the logs in winter when the slick snow and ice eased the drag, but homestead clearing was an anytime job. At the end of the logging day, Halvor and Tellif built a bonfire away from the shanty and threw the unneeded branches, bushes and saplings on the fire, leaving it to burn itself out.

Everybody in the family pitched in to remove the stumps in the fields, chopping, burning, wrapping with chain and yanking with oxen power. Even the youngest fed the fire set to burn out a stump. They plowed and sowed around the most stubborn stumps, letting them rot a few years before trying again. Tallak and the Germans muscled the plow, pulled by oxen or pushed with manpower, their mature bulk required even in this sandy soil. Melvin, seven, and even Mary, age five, helped with the sowing, and everyone except three-year-old Eli worked together to improve the log shanty, chinking any spaces between the logs with clay and lime to keep out the wind and snow of winter, adding shutters to the window openings. Window glass would come later in this northern wild. The crew built the privy, chicken coop, and root cellar before the first frost.

The crop of children was nearing perfection as their contribution to the homestead exceeded the cries and whimpers of babies. The Germans were still there, still unnamed, but now permanent hired help. Ellen and Tallak were echoing the husman tradition of Norway by providing food and shelter to the Germans in exchange for their labor.

Tallak contemplated moving the logs to the Gardner Sawmill

before winter set in. They were piling up at the log chute and he was anxious to earn the cash now, instead of waiting for the ice to freeze the bay for easier hauling. The family could use the cash to purchase furnishings for their new home, and add to their supply of produce and grain for the winter.

Lake dwellers had devised a method of moving logs from source to sawmill in water, using a logging raft, instead of waiting for the ice of winter. These rafts were sixteen by twelve, or sixteen by sixteen, with longer "boom logs" enclosing the logs to be transported. The raft was dragged by a scow rigged with windlass and rope. Scow and raft were connected by a four to five-hundred-foot rope, then the oarsmen rowed the scow until the rope was taut, dropped the scow anchor, manned the windlass to pull the raft close to the scow, dropped the raft anchor, rowed the scow another five hundred feet, and started all over again. Three or four raft sections were hauled in this way. A painstaking method, which could take days. Luckily F.B. Gardner, owner of the sawmill, built a steamboat tug a few years later, taking most of the pain away. This was a job for experts, who hired out for logging crews. Tallak and Ellen compared the costs of fall water rafting with winter sled hauling before deciding whether the early cash was worth the extra cost.

Ellen was leaning backwards with child at that first harvesting time in Sugar Creek, nonetheless she canned and dried and filled the cellar. Tellif and Halvor, reassigned from logging to harvesting (and perhaps canning) took time out to teach Melvin to split the wood for the kindling pile. Mary and Eli stacked the kindling and carried (small) pails of water to the kitchen, just to get the idea.

Tallak and Ellen loved their children no less than we do today, but unlike us, they also needed them to become working partners in the family enterprise. The children learned early that they were needed as coworker with their parents and siblings from the moment their little hands could carry a stick.

****

I was a privileged child growing up in the twentieth century. Seven years younger than my closest sibling, a spoiled "youngest-only," I seldom did the dishes. But when I was nine, I visited my Grandmother Carrie and her son Oliver on his farm in Forestville, Wisconsin. Uncle Oliver, a Norwegian bachelor farmer, was harvesting hay when I arrived, a difficult one-man job. He decided I was old enough to drive, introduced me to the enormous red tractor, hooked up the hay-wagon and hay-loader, set me down on the seat next to him, and drove this triple rig down the road to the hayfield. We made a glorious racket.

He centered the tractor on the first row. "Keep the front wheels straight so the rocks don't kick them off to the side, and hold on tight."

Oliver climbed up to the wagon-bed, shouted "Go" and began leveling the hay being pulled up by the hay loader. "Whoa." We were at the end of the row. I found the brake. Oliver climbed down to turn the tractor around and position the rig on the next row. I took over.

I took over! I felt like a million dollars — I was needed to do this simple chore that allowed Oliver to do the job in half the time.

I wonder. Did Halvor and Tellif feel that same pride in their contribution to the homestead? Expected to work hard and early, did it nonetheless feel good to realize that their chores were necessary not just to save a little time, but to assure their family's survival?

****

In any event, a child's life could turn exciting while engaging in one of those routine nineteenth century chores. Aunt Mary relates an early adventure:

> *When Melvin was about 10 years old [1860] and out in the woods looking for the cows, he saw a bear run into a hollow log. He plugged it up as best he could with the material at hand, and then ran home to get his father to come with his gun. When they returned they found the bear had worked his way out and escaped. (Danker, Interview with Aunt Mary.)*

In October of 1857, Christine was born, child number six to bless this family. This was Ellen's first lying-in without her mother or sisters near. Her sister Kirsten had been close by in Port Ulio, and before that her mother Marte was always with her when the birthing day came. Was there a midwife in this wilderness? Did these Norwegians mingle with the growing number of Belgians settling just down the road? A woman needed friends at birthing time. Whatever nationality, I hope Ellen had a midwife standing by.

The long nights of winter were welcomed. In this era when candles and gas lamps were frugally conserved, the darkness dictated a time to sleep, and as the nights lengthened, a time for two sleeps, with wakefulness in between. A time to play, if your partner was amorous. A time to remember, to muse, to pray — some called this luxurious interval "God's hour." Ellen might wonder in these wakeful hours — how her sisters and brothers were celebrating the Christmas season this year. Was Nella happy in Canada learning a Quaker Christmas, were Elias and Jens, in their established Norwegian communities, celebrating much like their childhood Christmas in Norway? Ellen would miss the early close-knit Port Ulio Christmases, she'd miss the Christmases of Norway, the *lutefisk* and *lefse*, julekake with its citron and cardamom — could she find those ingredients in Sugar Creek? Did she pack a *krumkaka* iron along with her kitchen supplies from Norway?

And her little sister Helene, the one "left behind" in Norway, how did she fare? Did she walk to the Bamble Kirke on Christmas Day with her new family, the Vinjes, as Ellen remembered walking with Helene and all the family so many years ago? Helene was twenty-five years old this December. Where was she now, who else did she walk with?

Chapter 17 — 1858 – Helene in Norway

Helene was dreaming of her wedding dress, which she soon would be designing and sewing with her step-mother Kari. Amund, her husband to be, was also her neighbor — his farm of Arnesplass was less than a half mile from the Vinje farm. The wedding was a year away, but Helene and Amund sometimes spent the night together — their engagement was sanction enough.

It's certain that Amund and Helene knew each other all their lives. The Arnesplass farm had been in Amund's family for several generations and Amund's oldest brother Christen sold the farm or some portion of it to Amund for 400 speciedallers in 1875, just one year before he married Helene.

Helene and Amund were both baptized and confirmed in the Bamble Kirke. A good thing — until 1912 Norway by statute required that evidence of confirmation be presented before a marriage could be performed.

If either or both had the luxury of schooling, they studied in the same classroom, the parlor of a neighboring farm where their teacher both taught and received room and board. School was held for a few months every year in each rural community, the teachers moving from town to town. They taught religion, reading, writing and sums to all ages, with religion considered the most important. The Lutheran church required several years of religion lessons prior to confirmation. If the religious classes taught by the roving teachers weren't sufficient, the parish priest or pastor taught their young flock. However, as in most nineteenth century rural cultures, school attendance took second place to farm-work or household chores.

Helene had been fourteen when her mother Marte and her entire family left for America from the Røskleven farm. Her adoptive parents, Kari and Lars were a big part of her life. Kari had some sad moments, knowing this gift of a daughter would soon be leaving her home. But she and Lars were getting older and might enjoy a quieter household. Helene wouldn't live far away.

And so Helene and Amund were married in November of 1858. Their marriage was documented in the Bamble Kirke parish register:

Brudgommens (bridegroom) Amund Christiansen, age 23, of Arnesplass

Bruden (bride) Helene Martine Halvorsdatter, age 25, of Røskleven (both the farm where Helene was born and her adopted farm, Vinje, were listed after her name.)

****

The farm name served as the identifier needed to sort out those similar names. The Norwegian Bygdebok, recording farm ownership throughout Norway, kept the history of farms from the fifteenth century forward. Two thick volumes were needed for the Bamble area alone. Volume II lists the individual farms of every resident of Bamble from 1814 to 1950. It includes the name of each owner, his parents, wife, and children, dates of marriages, birth and birthplace and death of each person. Farm yields and livestock, type of soil and availability of firewood on the land were listed for selected years. Each transfer of ownership detailed name of new owner, whether inheritance or sale and date and amount paid. For my ancestors, the date and destination of their emigration to America was added to the farm information.

Amund and Helene retained their farm identities as long as they lived on that farm. It was often used with their surname, Amund Christianson and Helene Halvorsdatter. I don't know if they adopted the name Arnes or Arnesplass in the years that they lived there.

****

I could hardly tear myself away from the Arnesplass farm during my 2015 Bamble visit. Part of the magic was the approach, orchestrated by my somewhat-removed cousin Monica. Remember, Tallak's mother was the second wife of Tallak's father, Tellif Amundson. Monica is the great-grandchild of Anders, the second son of wife number one. Monica, born and raised in Bamble, learned of her near-kin who had left Bamble for America and made it her mission to hunt down her American relatives. She found a clan of us in Door County, Wisconsin, and attended the first Haines family reunion in Sturgeon Bay in 2011. She has been part of the family ever since.

Now in my first visit to Bamble, Monica was my local guide. We had already visited the Høen farm, Smedplassen and Skjelbred. To visit Arnesplass, we drove to the Aby fjord harbor where Monica parked her car.

"We'll go the back way," said my guide, as she motioned to a trailhead across the street. We started up an immediately steep path, trekked up and up, sometimes glimpsing the fjord, mostly through deep woods on a path marked with an occasional blue blaze on a tree trunk, the Norwegian contemporary trail markers. Contemporary trail markers on an ancient trail. At one spot there was a rope hanging to assist a climb up steep rocks. Monica hopped up the rocks without it, but I welcomed its swinging assistance. After about three quarters of a mile, we stepped onto green grass surrounding the white shingled, open-gabled roofed home of my great-grandmother Helene, and the birthplace of our storyteller, my grandmother Carrie.

Arnesplass was beautiful. The home on its rocks seemed far above the waters yet in only ten or twelve rock hops I was on the shore. Forests and rocks surrounded the fjord, the rock shielding the fields and outbuildings from sea-storms on the water. Lilac trees bloomed on several rocky levels. I pictured Helene pausing her hoeing or escorting the cows from barn to pasture to gaze on the Aby fjord in its many moods. When we walked back down the path away from Arnesplass, I could feel Helene, with tiny Carrie in her arms, walking beside me.

****

Amund was both fisherman and farmer, so Helene, much like her sister Ellen in America, had much of the farm-work to tackle alone. The Bygdebok of Bamble announces that they had two cows and a pig on the farm and grew barley, oats, potatoes and hay.

Helene gave birth to her first child on April 23, 1859, five months after Helene and Amund were married. The baby was baptized on May 22 — her name Marte Karine, after Amund's mother, as was the tradition in Norway. Marte happened to be the name of Helene's mother also, a double blessing on the new baby. Helene's mother-in-law lived until 1881, and would be a visible grandmotherly presence in Marte's life.

But baby Marte would never know her maternal grandmother. Helene knew that her mother had emigrated to America in 1846, and might have heard of her death in Port Ulio through earlier letters from friends who had emigrated and lived there. In those long nights of the Norway winter Helene had time to think about her missing family — her mother Marte, six brothers and sisters, her brother-in-law Tallak, just gone. Had they survived the perils of life in America? Life remained tough in Norway, food scarce some years, crop yields unpredictable. Did Helene and Amund consider emigrating?

Not now. Not yet.

Chapter 18 — 1860 – Trinkets, Ponies and Schooling

As Helene and Amund began their family in Bamble, her sister Ellen was in her eighth pregnancy, chasing after two-year-old Christine and managing her household in the wilderness of Sugar Creek.

Ellen might have been handling things on her own for much of the time that summer. Once the spring plowing and sowing were done, Tallak had other business to attend to:

Tallack Haines was now for a time an Indian trader. He used to travel to Milwaukee where he bought a store of merchandise, especially glittery trinkets which the Indians like and used. With this merchandise he visited the Indians and sold or traded for horses. These horses he took home to Sugar creek where he fed them until they were fat and sleek. Then he took them to Green Bay or Milwaukee and sold them. He did very well with this business.

Historian Hjalmar Holand wrote those words in an article published in 1922 entitled *Hainesville, an Old Seaman's Paradise,* the "old Seaman" none other than Tallak himself. Mr. Holand gathered the stories for his histories by interviewing Norwegian immigrants, "roaming Door County on a bicycle when its roads were only trails," between 1885 and 1908; Tallak was seventy-three in 1885, and lived to age ninety-four. It appears that Hjalmer had an exclusive — Tallak's adventures as told by Tallak.

I doubt the Indians remaining in the area were still being taken in by a wily Norwegian trading "glittery trinkets." I suspect my great-grandfather told a colorful tale, which combined with Mr. Holand's editorial license might create an embellished story.

The local Native Americans traditionally traded for colored cloth and farming tools, axes, hoes and knives in exchange for furs, sometimes fish and game, and, now we know, horses. Holand, in his book *History of Door County*, noted that in 1835 there was a village of more than five hundred Menominees and Chippewas on the east side of Little Sturgeon near its mouth. "Here was a good place for bartering," he added. Perhaps the village still existed in Tallak's time. The natives remaining in the area in 1857 had been trading with the white man for many years and might teach Tallak some parleying skills. But I'm sure Tallak was trading, and for the best deal possible.

****

The story is one more example of the complete omission of women and children in the histories written in that time. Hjalmer Holand writes his long essay on Tallak's life, with never an acknowledgment of his wife or his children. "He" is all there is. Never another pronoun, not even a "they." Add this short story of one man to the myriad of histories written through the ages — all applying the same principle. Women were automatically an extension of the man, as were children.

One can't fault the historians, nor Hjalmer. They were reporting the world as it was — Tallak wouldn't think of mentioning his family. Family was assumed. Bachelorhood was noteworthy. But women were beginning to squirm under this philosophy. Their cocoons were splitting apart, the butterfly struggling to emerge.

But change comes slowly with such ingrained ideologies. Ideologies embraced by both men and women. We are still squirming.

****

On August 18, 1860, my grandfather Oscar was born, the seventh child. No baptism for Oscar; Tallak and Ellen seemed convinced that only a bona fide Norwegian Lutheran baptism could properly bless their children. Oscar would be twelve years old before the first Lutheran Church was organized in Door County. The children born in Port Ulio had been properly baptized as infants in the Holden Norwegian Lutheran church, along with a two-year delayed baptism for Tellif, born in Canada. Tallak and Ellen had spurned a Canadian Quaker or Anglican church baptism for Tellif; no chance that St. Mary's Catholic church in Sugar Creek would be trusted with Oscar's soul.

Tallak and Ellen maintained the Norwegian naming traditions for their first few children — Gunhild was named for Tallak's mother, first son Halvor for Ellen's father, not Tallak's — second son Tellif got Tallak's father's name. The names Marie, Elias and Christine honor Ellen's mother and siblings. Melvin and Oscar don't match any known family ancestors. All-American names.

Hopefully Tallak was home for this birth, perhaps training the ponies. But Halvor, now sixteen, could run for the midwife and boil the water. Thirteen-year-old Tellif could supervise Melvin, Mary, Elias and Christine. Sure. And it's not like this birth event was anything Ellen couldn't handle — she was pregnant most of the time. Still — I'd like to think that Tallak was there too — to celebrate the birth of my grandfather.

****

Hjalmar Holand's story highlights the changed circumstances of the homestead. With Germans and two grown boys to leave back on the farm, Tallak could roam. He had a horse to ride, perhaps a wagon or carriage for the improved roads. He had business to attend to. His travels to Green Bay and Milwaukee were certainly extended to points along Lake Michigan: Port Washington, Manitowoc and Algoma. Perhaps he bunked with in-laws who were spread around the state.

Ellen had the children all to herself much of the time. The

State of Wisconsin had passed legislation creating a free public-school system in 1848 and early schools were set up in private residences in Sturgeon Bay beginning in 1856. By 1858 there was a school in Union and two in Brussels, but it is questionable whether Ellen and Tallak's children could, or would, attend. Like the Port Ulio German-speaking schools, here French or Walloon — the language spoken in many parts of Belgium and carried over the ocean with the Belgians — was likely the language spoken in the early schools of Union.

Melvin (age ten when Oscar was born) describes their schooling in a later biography:

> *As the surrounding country was wholly undeveloped at the time, the educational advantages were very limited. . . [we] children received but a meager amount of schooling.*

Ellen didn't teach from textbooks, but she schooled her children. Her school was year-round, no holidays or summer vacations, no opportunity to play hooky. Summer and winter each had their own curriculum — outdoor lessons of farming and gardening, herb and berry gathering in summer, indoor home craft seminars in winter — stitchery skills, candle dipping, whittling and carpenter workshops for creating tools and buckets. Cooking skills continued summer and winter — kneading the flakiest biscuits, blending herbs for a fragrant soup. These were the lessons in Ellen's schoolhouse. Reading and writing might not be Ellen's skills but calculations certainly were; apportioning food stores to last the winter, or calculating the best return on trades of excess produce, grain and timber, measuring crop, produce, egg and milk production.

Despite Tallak's travels, he co-taught with Ellen. The boys particularly learned by participating with Tallak on every task of the homestead. They learned to log, handle oxen teams, maneuver logs to sawmills. They navigated the waters in rowboats and scows, and gentled and trained the ponies Tallak brought home. The older boys traveled with Tallak, learning negotiation skills and Wisconsin geography.

Ellen and Tallak taught, but the wild times and wild creatures held their own lessons for their babies; these children learned early to take care of themselves. Aunt Mary relates one day's adventure:

> *the children saw a bear coming toward the house, with a dog after it, and they closed the door and all pressed their weight against it, but the bear, being chased himself, had no notion of chasing the children, ran past the house and into the woods.* (Danker, *Interview with Aunt Mary*)

Long ago in Norway, Tallak and Ellen had lost their first child within days of her birth, but now seven healthy Hoens, slowly morphing into Haineses, worked and romped around their homestead. But on April 12, 1861, Confederate forces fired upon Ft. Sumter, and these new Americans, in the wilderness of northern Wisconsin, found themselves at war.

On February 18, 1862, Halvor enlisted in the 15th Wisconsin Infantry Regiment in Madison, Wisconsin.

Chapter 19 — 1862 – Civil War in Sugar Creek

In early 1862, President Lincoln called for an additional army of 300,000 men. The quota for the State of Wisconsin was 11,904 men between the ages of 18 and 45, and the news was spread that if that quota was not met a draft would be established. In March of 1863 the Enrollment Act did mandate the draft of men between the ages of 20 and 45, but Halvor, age 17, had enlisted one year earlier. On March 1, 1862, he was sworn into Company F of the 15th Wisconsin Infantry Regiment at Camp Randall, Madison, Wisconsin.

> *Oliver Haines, eldest son of Tallak Haines of Brussels, also went out with the Fifteenth. Oliver, like all the Scandinavians, is true blue, and ready to do his full part at the front. (ADV, 1862-06-07)*

Halvor [Oliver] was seventeen when he enlisted; he was seventeen when he died.

Volume 1, Issue 1 of the *Door County Advocate* was published on Saturday, March 22, 1862, the launching issue of the first newspaper published in Door County. Poems, prose and praise for the new publication filled the first page; those early newspapers left the hard news for page two. This page two pronounced a "celebration":

> *The Glorious War News. We are obliged to lay over for our next issue, several articles, in order to make way for the glorious war news. Glory! glory! glory!! follows our gallant and victorious forces at every step, the rebels are falling back at every point, and are fast approaching the last scene in this terrible and wicked tragedy.*

Would that this optimistic account of early victory had

prevailed. The *Advocate* was one hundred percent behind the Union cause. It remained optimistic and stoutly Union throughout the war, through all the terrible tolls that war demanded.

Halvor received $100 (about $1,500 in 2015 dollars) as advanced bounty when he enlisted and $13.00 ($195 in 2015) as one month's advance pay. That alone might have been reason to sign up. The threat of an imminent Enrollment Act and the local fervor for this war added to his resolve. An in-person encouragement from Colonel Hans Christian Heg, the leader of the 15th would clinch it. Colonel Heg toured the small towns of the State of Wisconsin to encourage immigrants to join his Norwegian-language regiment. The bloody statistics of these battles seemed buried in victory rhetoric.

On March 2, 1862, Halvor and his 875 fellow recruits, "composed of the best bone and sinew of the Northwest" (*DCA*,1862-03-22), marched off in a snowstorm from the courthouse steps in Madison to the train station and boarded the train to Chicago. From there the troops continued by train to Alton, Illinois. They boarded a steamer on the Mississippi, and steamed through St. Louis to the training camp for new recruits, Camp Lyon, at Bird's Point, Missouri, across the river from Cairo, Illinois.

> *Private letters from some of the boys [in the 15th regiment] say they were hurried through in double-quick time — having no time to even take their boots off, from the time they left Sturgeon Bay, until they arrived in Cairo. (DCA, 1862-03-29)*

Did Tallak ride with Halvor to Madison, to keep him company and act as his guide? Was he in the snowstorm cheering his son and the 15th, when they marched off to war?

The Camp Lyon training went quickly, and in mid-March the troops returned to Cairo to board a steamship headed down the Mississippi River to New Madrid, Missouri. Here the river made a tight double turn, with Island #10 at the base. When the Wisconsin 15th arrived, the battle called "Island #10" had been going for a week, and troops of 25,000 were gathering under Brigadier General John Pope and his Army of the Mississippi. Pope ordered two gunboats down from Cairo on March 14, beginning the siege. The battle lasted until April 8, with casualties on both sides surprisingly low. In the end the North held the island — an important victory for the Union because it opened up the Mississippi River. Just three weeks later New Orleans was captured. I wonder if Halvor realized that he fought in a battle of major importance in this uncivil Civil War.

****

Right away, they missed him. Things weren't the same in Sugar Creek with Halvor away in the war. Tallak missed his original right-hand man, perhaps his closest male companion in the six or so years they had worked side by side. Tellif and Melvin missed the man-boy who had coached and tutored them as they graduated to the heavier chores of plowing, logging, harvesting. The younger at-home siblings all missed Halvor's teasing and banter when he returned from his work in the fields and the forests. Ellen worried, reading or listening to discussions of the latest news of the 15th regiment, flinching at each fatality statistic. Praying that this war would end soon, as the press continued to predict.

Twelve-year-old Melvin might be recruited to help fill the gap on the logging team when Halvor left, and guiltily relish the opportunity to join Tellif and his father. Tellif, 15, and Melvin (almost a teenager) were captivated by the new horse-drawn threshing machine that Tallak brought home the October after Halvor went off to war, embracing this new technology with the enthusiasm of teenagers throughout time.

More Threshing Machines

Tallak Hayne, of the town of Brussels, has just returned home with a good threshing Machine. We should think this will be a great boon to our Belgian citizens in the south part of the county, and Tallak will doubtless find plenty of work up there, but we would inform our readers that he is ready to take his machine into any of the adjoining towns where he may be wanted. When Tallak takes hold of anything he does it right up to the handle. (DCA, 1862-10-04)

Tallak and his crew had to hustle to keep up with the competition. Mr. J. Christensen brought his threshing machine to Sturgeon Bay in the same month. His rates: "Wheat 5 cents a bushel, Oats three and a half . . . Rye and Barley four cents per bushel." (*DCA*, 1862-09-20)

In the five years since they first settled in Sugar Creek, much had changed in the family and in their world. Their immediate neighborhood was now populated with Belgians. The Belgian settlements had spread to the town of Union, and fifteen-thousand Belgians eventually settled in the contiguous Door, Brown and Kewaunee Counties.

Little Sturgeon continued to overshadow Sturgeon Bay as the center of commerce in 1862, thanks to Freeland B. Gardner, who ran two sawmills, a gristmill, a general store, and a shipyard. Mr. Gardner operated multiple lumber camps in winter, and at one time employed 400 men from Brussels, Union and Gardner villages. Tallak, logging for Mr. Gardner, learned a lot about running a camp, storing ideas for his future Nasawaupee camps. Tallak looked forward to welcoming Halvor back as his logging partner.

The logs were transported by ship to Green Bay or Chicago — schooners and brigs were still sailing the waters of Green Bay, but steam-powered ships were soon to overrun the wind-driven sailing ships, and Gardner's shipyard was jumping on the steamboat. In 1862, his shipyard unveiled a steam-driven side-wheeler tug for his timber-towing business, 110 feet long with a 26-foot beam. The *Door County Advocate* touted this invention as "furnishing Door County and the east shore with steam facilities to connect with the railroad in Green Bay."

Green Bay waters remained the highway of Door County; there was still no good wagon road from Sturgeon Bay to the town of Green Bay. The lobbying for such a road had begun; the need well stated by a gentleman from Manitowoc in a letter to the editor noting:

> *while some people worry that the noise of the wagons would "scare the hens off their nests," he disagrees, and asserts "A finely traveled highway is as essential to the progress of a new settlement as the press. One renders the home accessible to the outside world, the other to the mind."*

Ellen and the family benefited too from Mr. Gardner's Dry Goods Establishment, sporting a full column ad every week in the *Advocate*: "Largest Stock of Goods!" "Bring your wife or sweetheart!"

> *Dry Goods, prints, lawns, ginghams, sheeting, skirting, checks, stripes, denims, kentucky jane, flannels, linsey woolsey, batting, table covers, cassimeres, satinets, ribbon, linen, hoop-skirts . . . Yankee notions, in endless varieties . . .*

> *Ready made clothing, groceries, crockery and glassware, farming tools, saw mill and grist mill, lamps and kerosene, tinware and Syracuse salt. All kinds of produce taken in exchange for goods . . . Cash never refused. (DCA, 1862-08-09)*

The ready-made cloth simplified the chores of the household, shuffling the spinning wheel off to the attic, perhaps even eliminating the sheep from the family livestock. Ellen and the girls still sewed their dresses and petticoats, the shirts and pants and long underwear for their men and boys, but hats, caps, boots and shoes were available ready-made at the store, eliminating some traditional knitting projects. The women cut and hemmed the towels and bedclothes, but table covers and hoop-skirts were theirs for cash or trade. The mending, of course, remained never-ending. Ellen was eying the newfangled sewing machine now available in Green Bay, something to suggest to Tallak when he went on his next trading excursion.

Ellen welcomed the time-saving improvements — probably thought it was about time for household innovations to match the farming gadgets. It helped too that Mary, at age ten, was in the advanced stages of her homestead internship, and Eli, although itching to join the older boys at his great age of eight, was pretty handy with most farming chores. Assuming the two Germans were still with the family, Eli might tag along with them for advance training. Christine helped too, corralling and entertaining Oscar, just two.

Ellen was holed up in the shanty with her younger charges for the coldest months of winter, when logging camps flourished. Summer too held long days with Tallak and the boys off horse trading, and now roving the county with the threshing machine. Spring and fall might have found the entire family working together to complete the plowing, planting and harvesting.

But even though Ellen was long accustomed to the absence of her son Halvor as he spent his days with Tallak, this absence was deeper, and as the summer advanced, her mind flew to her son when chores lightened. Hopefully Ellen had friends down the road, whatever ethnicity, to share a cup of coffee with on lonely days. There were other women in the neighborhood who had sons and sometimes husbands off to the war as well, who would wonder with Ellen where their men were, and how they were faring.

Chapter 20 — 1862 – Halvor

Ellen bore her last child, Martha Eliza (Lizzie) on January 15, 1863. Ellen was forty-six years old. The relatively mild early winter of that year might have eased her final pregnancy, but in the night of December thirty-first, the temperature dropped sharply with a fierce northwest wind, a winter long remembered for its bitter cold. A tough world for Lizzie's debut. For Ellen's final lying-in.

In a document prepared just two months after Lizzie's birth, the parents and children are listed in a manner that seems to announce the completion of this family. It is an elegant, official looking document, obviously written for the family by a scrivener in a beautiful hand.

Tallak Tellefsen, born in Norway on the 28th of September 1812,
Wife Ellen Christine Halvorsdaughter, born in Norway on the 14th of May 1817.Their children are
1st Halvor, born on the 3d of December 1845,
2nd Tellif born on the 12th of August 1847,
3d Melvin born on the 7th of January 1850,
4th Maria Tallette Christine born on the 4th of February 1852,
5th Elias born on the 20th of May 1854,
6th Christine born on the 14th day of October 1857,
7th Oscar born on the 8th of September 1860,
8th Martha Eliza born on the 15th of January 1863.
We are all in America, Door Co. Wis.

Dated this 15th of March 1863.

This document is a puzzle. The reversion to Tallak and Ellen's Norwegian surnames, which they hadn't used in America for many years, suggests it was written to inform those left behind in their native country. Written to let them know their family was thriving. And yet, Grandma Carrie's family history states that her mother Helene never received a communication from anyone in her family between 1857 and 1881. Perhaps the post to Norway was lost in the Civil War chaos. But the biggest puzzle is that there is no mention of Halvor's death six months before the document's date. Did they wish to deny that one was lost?

Or had they not yet heard?

****

I read the hard facts on a lovely sunny day in 2015. The strongbox lay on the table, open when I arrived at my cousin's Sand Bay cottage. Some things to show you, he said. My cousin pulled out a faded fragile paper entitled: The Army of the United States — Inventory of Effects of Deceased Soldier. The document had been handed down to my cousin from his father Tallack (Ted), who got it from his father Oscar, delivered into Oscar's hands by his father, Tallak. (Spelled Tallack by family by the time of Ted's birth.)

The name Halvor Hoen is carefully written over the original name of Oliver Haines. On the Certification section, Oliver Haines is crossed out, and Halvor Hoen written in after it. Someone insisted that the name on this Inventory match the name written in the Bamble parish baptismal records seventeen years before his death — Halvor Høen, only the slashed "o" is different.

114

The document continues: Enlisted February 18, 1862, born Norway, Europe, age seventeen, five feet six inches tall, light complexion, blue eyes, light hair, occupation farmer. Died in the hospital at Jackson, Tennessee on September 27, 1862. His possessions, enumerated on a pre-printed checklist: one great coat, one uniform coat, one flannel stack coat, one pr trowsers, two flannel shirts, one pr shoes, one pr socks, one canteen and specie $25.00. Unchecked possibilities: blanket, drawers (neither flannel nor cotton), boots, forage cap, uniform jacket. Cause of death: Chronic Diarrhea.

****

When did Tallak and Ellen receive this document?

Halvor had already died when Tallak purchased the threshing machine in October. Halvor had already died when Lizzie was born in December. Halvor had already died when Tallak and Ellen created the record of their family "all now in America."

Except one would not be home again.

Perhaps the delayed news of Halvor's death sent the optimistic document quietly into a drawer, set aside to puzzle and sadden descendants decades in the future.

****

The 15th Wisconsin Infantry Regiment lost 94 men in battle, 241 men from disease. Over 10,000 soldiers from the State of Wisconsin died in the Civil War. It is hard to imagine those numbers, but it helps us to understand that more than six months could go by before Tallak and Ellen knew of Halvor's death. The governments of both the North or the South did not have the staff or organization to notify families of their losses. Notification letters and telegrams were often composed by friends of the deceased soldier, or by a nurse or doctor in the hospital; sometimes the first notice was an article in a local newspaper.

Halvor would have been hurriedly buried in the hospital burying grounds, but by 1866 his body might be one of the 4,000 unknown Union soldiers whose bodies were exhumed after the war and buried in the Corinth National Cemetery in Corinth, Mississippi. The resting place was designated for Union soldiers who had been buried in the battlefields or on hospital grounds during the war throughout northern Mississippi, Alabama and southern Tennessee. The U.S. Department of Veterans Affairs confirms that by 1870, the Corinth cemetery contained 5,688 interments, including almost 4,000 unknown dead, all Union soldiers except for two known and one unknown Confederate soldiers.

I walked among those 4,000 white markers, some tall, some curved, some square, going on forever, finally in the symmetry of the marching units desired by generals, symmetry that seldom happened with these ragtag Civil War children soldiers. I walked among the nameless, the four-digit numbers, knowing that Halvor Høen or Haines was not on the list of named soldiers buried here, neither online or at the adjacent volunteer center. But I went anyway. One of those nameless might be my great-great uncle. Or a comrade. It seemed appropriate to visit this southern cemetery honoring the northern dead.

****

Thirty-three years after Halvor's death, Oscar and Carrie would name their firstborn son Oliver Thomas Haines.

116

Chapter 21 — 1863 – The Belgians

They had lived in Sugar Creek for seven or eight years, during which time Tallak probably logged with his Belgian neighbors, and later rented his threshing machine to Belgian farmers. But Hjalmer Holand, in his "Old Seaman's Paradise" article, put an alternate spin on the Sugar Creek years:

Since he [Tallak] *was the first settler by Sugar creek, he hoped to establish a Norwegian settlement there. That dream came to nothing. Shortly after, an army of Belgians . . . came by the thousands like a swarm of grasshoppers. A whole ship which was loaded with Belgians was shipwrecked by a hard storm near where* [Tallak] *had built his home. . . the ship had a large shipment of potatoes so for weeks there was a procession of Belgians carrying sacks of Potatoes farther into the woods. In a short time, all the land 40 miles to the north and to the south was taken up by the Belgians. . . it became the largest Belgian settlement in America.*

These Belgians were a hard-working people but they had some bad habits in their behavior which they still retain. Their greatest pleasure was to assemble in drinking parlors or saloons. . . Each Sunday there was a large crowd of people at each saloon singing or hollering. This was their understanding of the Sunday Rest. . . When they had paid their tithes and recited the Pator Noster and Ave Maria . . . the important thing was to drink as much brandy as possible so they could forget their wood chopping and other everyday work. The celebrations were terrible.

Tallack Haines lived with these wild men as long as he could stand it. At last, he became so tired and

> *disgusted with their behavior that he sold his farm for a few dollars and moved away from there.* (Hjalmar "Hainesville")

Whew! I'm not sure I like this intolerant Tallak. But since we have established that Mr. Holand probably interviewed Tallak some twenty years after this event, I can't deny that this is another example of "Tallak's adventures as told by Tallak." Is this how he remembered his Belgian neighbors — immigrants like him who had suffered in the old country, and emigrated to improve their lot? Did Tallak never have a spot of ale on his day of rest?

I suspect the Belgians had some words to describe their Norwegian neighbors, *a sanctimonious, dour, colorless people.*

My grandmother Carrie also had plenty of time to talk with her father-in-law Tallak. He lived with her and her husband Oscar in his last years. Carrie describes the reason for the Sugar Creek move in dramatically different terms:

> *Oliver went into the Army* [Civil war] *and died of some sickness after six months. His father, Tallak, felt so bad about that death that he did not want to live in Sugar creek any more so they moved on to Sturgeon Bay. They lived there for a while, then Tallak bought the point which is known as Idlewild.* (Carrie, *History*)

I have no basis to argue about the words Tallak might have shared with Mr. Holand, but I repeat that Tallak had lived with these folks for seven years, their numbers and proximity assuring interaction on many matters, in many activities. And Tallak didn't "sell his farm for a few dollars;" when he did sell, several years after he left the area, the sales price was three times the amount he had paid to the government for the land nine years earlier.

Mr. Holand was a colorful writer. His history volumes are rambling, not formally cited, and thus have been dismissed by some scholars. But this is 19th century anecdotal writing, by an author who talked to these immigrants. The dates and locations of his Tallak anecdotes corroborate with public and family records — and the details are delicious.

I shall use them with abandon.

But not without scrutiny.

Not without checking with my grandmother first.

It wasn't surprising that the family would head up the road to Sturgeon Bay, probably in early 1863, after the spring thaw, after they had news of Halvor's death. Tallak still owned the one-hundred-acre plot that he had purchased in Big Creek in 1857. The family may have stopped there. The newspaper reported that Tallak was building a house in April of 1863 — no location given— but Big Creek was the only property he owned at that time. His name appeared because he fell from the scaffold. The article added that he broke no bones, but it was feared he would be laid up for some time. This was the first of many proclamations of Tallak's prolonged disability or death; the *Advocate* was right only once.

****

I'm going with my grandmother's reasoning for this move. I would add that it wasn't only Tallak who "felt so bad about that death." Count Ellen at the top of the list with Tallak, Tellif, Melvin, Mary, Eli right below, and Christine, Oscar and even little Lizzie, three months old, not understanding the death, but feeling the sadness of the family around them. Watch these babies doing silly and adorable things to swing the moods of their unhappy family — to make their world happy again. Ellen and Tallak took the extra step of moving themselves away from the place where the pain began.

Chapter 22 — 1863 – Sturgeon Bay

The town of Sturgeon Bay was first called "Otumba." Before that it had several names for the scattered saw mills and worker settlements on the shores of Sturgeon Bay. The State of Wisconsin officially recognized the town of "Otumba" in 1857, the second "official" town in Door County. Three years later the County approved the name change to Sturgeon Bay.

The town sat on the northeast shore of a bay that stretched eight miles inland from Green Bay. The bay had been known as Sturgeon from before written history, named by the Indians because of the large number of Sturgeon [fish] then found in its waters. Father Allouez, the first missionary to the territory, was also the first to mention the bay in writing in 1676. He might have used the  portage trail between Lake Michigan and Sturgeon Bay, traversed for centuries by Indians, then missionaries and fur traders. These early travelers carried or dragged their canoes and scows less than two miles from Lake Michigan to Sturgeon Bay to shorten their sea voyage from the town of Green Bay to points south by over one hundred miles. The idea of linking those waters with a ship canal following the route of the portage trail was discussed as early as 1860.

When Tallak and Ellen arrived, the village of Sturgeon Bay contained several saw mills, a couple dozen houses, one small general store, the Cedar Street House hotel and the newly completed Sturgeon Bay Moravian Church. The saw mills were still struggling but their glory years were coming soon.

The family might have settled on the Big Creek acreage Tallak had purchased in 1857, into the house completed by Tallak during the Sugar Creek years. Tallak would already know the neighbors.

Tallak knew the town well enough to realize that Sturgeon Bay was not the place for a Norwegian settlement. He had been exploring the area since 1857, and probably visited often. By 1862 he had served as a juror for the County Court in Sturgeon

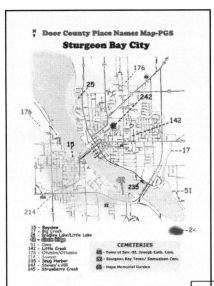

In 1860, Bay View (15) and Big Creek (17) Bradley or Little Lake (25), and maybe Cove (51) and Little Creek (142) would be familiar names to Tallak and Ellen.

Bay and pocketed $5.64 for that service. He knew the place and the people.

And he knew that the people represented a hodgepodge of nationalities — by 1881 Nasawaupee Township included Yankees from New York, Connecticut, Massachusetts, many of them second generation Englishmen; others direct from Germany, Prussia, Ireland, Sweden, Holland, Denmark, Canada and France. Oh yes, and some Norwegians. The Norwegian settlement idea had to wait.

****

I learned about those neighbors at the Door County Historical Society Heritage Village, located at the area still called Big Creek. Summer, 2014, I had just begun writing this book. The Village depicts rural life from 1880 to 1910, and contains a fish house, granary and blacksmith shed, one-room school, general store, and a replica of the Ephraim Moravian Church. The Historical Society's newest acquisition was the Hanson House.

It was built by Hans Hanson, Jr who emigrated from Hurum, not too far north of Bamble in southeast Norway, in 1853 and purchased the Big Creek property in 1857, the same year as Tallak's acquisition. In 2012, it was discovered that the original log structure of the Hanson House was a unique example of traditional Scandinavian construction — built with a concave log stacked on top of a tight fitting convex log with moss in between. Few immigrants were skilled in that building method, but Mr. Hanson had been a carpenter and ship builder in Norway.

Both Hans Hanson's property and Tallak's were in Section 9, Range 27, Township 26. Hans's is in the northeast quarter and Tallak's in the southeast quarter. Their properties shared a border.

These two families had a lot in common. Hans and his wife Berthe had six children by 1861, matching the ages of Tallak and Ellen's seven. If the family moved into this property for a time, it appears they would be compatible neighbors. The Historical Society has dug deeply into the family story of Hans and his family, but unfortunately there is nothing about the neighbors.

Hans had been active in the early effort of the Norwegian Moravian church to join the Lutherans, Quakers and Methodists to build a United Church. An encouraging example of cooperation among the early religious groups, effectively squelched by a Wisconsin State Law that the deed to a church building must be in the name of one organized church. The Moravians persevered on their own and in 1864 dedicated the first church building in Sturgeon Bay. The Czech-Moravian reformer John Hus preceded Martin Luther by a century. Hus was burned at the stake in 1415, but the religion continued, was wiped out by persecutions in the Thirty Years War, and yet thrived again in the 1700s. Perhaps the Hansons invited my great-grandparents to a Sunday service. Jon Hus was just an early Martin Luther.

Tallak had also purchased a few acres in the village of Bayview, on the west side of the waters of Sturgeon Bay. A fellow Norwegian, the ferryman E.T. Schjoth, sold him the land with a mortgage for $200 at 10% interest. The Haines children of all ages might have liked living in town for a while. Tallak's land was next door to the ferry crossing, a convenience only a few years old. The first ferryman, Mr. Fuller, had devised a craft for the bay crossing by fastening two large canoes together with a beam and covering them in planking to transfer teams and wagons across the bay. The canoe invention was lightweight and allowed an easy tow across the water: fifty cents for team and wagon, ten cents for foot passengers. If it was still around, it would have fascinated the Haines youngsters. When Mr. Schjoth took over in 1864, he used a heavier scow for the transfer of teams, with passengers manning the huge oars, still paying full fare. Later Schjoth stretched a rope across the bay and the scow was pulled across, hand-over-hand. Probably passenger hands.

This in-town interlude might be the time for those Haines

children to get some schooling. Chores were lighter for the town kids. The first school in Sturgeon Bay had a few pupils as early as 1856 — school was held for just a few months each year.

In May of 1863 Tallak joined the newly formed Union Club, a group supporting the Republicans in crushing the "unholy rebellion," the Civil War. (*DCA*, 1863-05-07) Tallak's fervor for the cause was not diminished by Halvor's death, perhaps, in fact, augmented by it. The Door County Advocate kept the war news upbeat, misleadingly so, but more and more Door County sons and husbands were on the battlefield or in a makeshift wartime cemetery. The club surprisingly welcomed both men and women — even printed the names of the women who joined the club, both married and unmarried, the wives or sisters of men in the war.

Tallak was an early subject of *Advocate* articles and over the years his name consistently appeared in the Sturgeon Bay and later Nasawaupee "news" columns. Tallak became a character.

Not Ellen. I hunted for Ellen's name in the *Advocate's* monthly member listings of the Union Club, this rare instance where the existence of women was acknowledged in print. Granted, every woman's first name was either "Mrs." or "Miss" with surname of husband or father. Mrs. Haine, however, was not among them.

Ellen was perhaps too busy with unpacking amidst seven children and Tallak falling off scaffolding and for that matter, she wondered how long Tallak would be content in town. Her man seemed more comfortable in remote spots away from town.

Ellen remained anonymous, as did most women, despite their priceless contribution to the family, to the whole of civilization. The anonymity of women was the culture of the day, protected by men, accepted by women. But Susan B. Anthony and Elizabeth Cady Stanton were standing in the wings.

Chapter 23 — 1864 – Idlewild Peninsula

Ellen's intuition was right. The Sturgeon Bay residency didn't last.

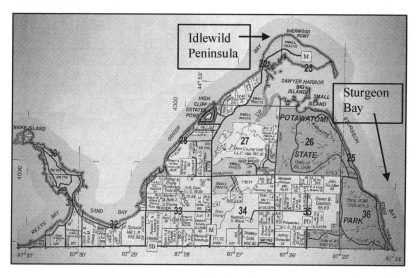

In May of 1864, Tallak purchased 102 acres from Benjamin F. and Matilda Sawyer on the narrow peninsula eventually called Idlewild in the township of Nasawaupee. The Idlewild peninsula was about seven miles west of the village of Bayview by land, five by water. It was surrounded by water on three sides: Green Bay on the north, Sturgeon Bay on the east and Sawyer's Harbor on the south. Its widest point was little more than a mile. On the peninsula's land connection, the forest of pine and hardwoods extended south on flat, swampy land, most of it government owned. The family was back in the wilderness again, their only road to town a row or sailboat in summer, sled in winter.

If the family didn't move to Idlewild at the time of the purchase or shortly thereafter, they might have been forced out of their Big Creek home in July of 1864, when the *Advocate* reported a fire in the Big Creek area. Tallak's house and other property burned to the ground, to the value of five hundred dollars. His neighbor, Hans Hanson, lost his barn and a fence, and a sawmill nearby lost over three thousand dollars in lumber. (*SBA*, 1864-07-02) With any luck, the Hainses and their possessions were safe in their new Idlewild home by that time.

The seller of the Idlewild property, Frank Sawyer, had located on "the point west of the bay" fourteen years before Tallak and Ellen arrived. He cleared the land and built his home, and legend has it that he sowed and harvested the first crop of wheat in Door County and that he made a living hunting, trapping and trading with the Indians. Sawyer's Harbor, the cozy bay jutting off the south side of Sturgeon Bay, was named after him.

Idlewild was remote and as wild as Sugar Creek when they first arrived, but this time the family moved into the home that Mr. Sawyer had built, not a "shanty."

Aunt Mary recalls their neighbors:

After the Sawyers were gone the only neighbors (except the Sherwoods) were the Indians, among them Chief Ninnecans. Whenever the Haines butchered cattle, they gave the Indians all parts of the animals that they could not use, including the entrails, and the natives soon had a fire going, cooked everything and had a big feast. (Danker)

"The Sherwoods" at the time Tallak and Ellen arrived referred to only Mrs. Sherwood. Peter and Clarissa Sherwood had settled on the point thirty years earlier, but Peter died in 1862, leaving Clarissa "penniless" despite the prosperous business he had conducted as cooper, making barrels for the fishing industry. For years it was believed that he had buried his treasure somewhere on the peninsula, but it was never found. Clarissa stayed on their homestead for several years after her husband's death.

Ellen and Clarissa shared a cup of coffee occasionally,

confirmed by the tale told by Hjalmer Holand that when Clarissa left her home for good, she dug up her prized apple tree that had grown from a seed planted by a sea captain friend many years before, and gave the tree to Ellen. In 1868 Clarissa Sherwood moved to Pennsylvania and sold her 196 acres to Tallak. Tallak then owned at least three hundred Idlewild acres. Neither Ellen's name nor the generic "and wife" were yet mentioned on real estate deeds.

Tallak signed his deeds with an "X," certified by a notary to be the mark of Tallak Hoen, or Henn or Haine. When the time came for Ellen to sign with him, she mimicked her husband with her own "X" signature.

It suggests illiteracy, that "X," but the business dealings negotiated by Tallak required an understanding of contracts, deeds and mortgages. Either he read the fine print, or hired someone to read it for him. In addition, Tallak was negotiating property deals, offering his threshing services in multiple townships and trading horses and "trinkets" with the various Indian tribes remaining on the peninsula. Tallak may have been unable to read or write either Norwegian or English when he first arrived in America, but after living in the United States for sixteen years I suspect he understood and spoke a few pertinent words in German, French and Walloon, and how to converse with the Menominee and Chippewa. As for English, Tallak was an original subscriber to the *Door County Advocate*, the first newspaper published in Door County. And Ellen? Assuming Tallak brought the paper home, if Ellen became curious, she would learn. It took a careful scanning of the newspaper to spot past-due tax sales, those lands available for the cost of taxes due, a bargain that Tallak took full advantage of and Ellen was beginning to take an interest in. Besides, neither Tallak nor Ellen would want to miss the intimate news of the neighborhood, and the neighbors, that took up the bulk of the newspaper pages.

Illiterate? I don't think so.

Why did the "X" continue? Tradition, ease, eccentricity?

Ellen's "X" was not yet required on the deeds, but if Tallak was flourishing, Ellen had his back. Still with a nursing baby and active toddler, Ellen maintained the homestead, the CEO of the family. Her two girls, Mary and Christine, and ten- year-old Eli were her current crew. When the *Advocate* got the news that Tallak lost three or four sheep to wolves (*SBA*,1866-09-21), you can bet it was Ellen and the children who tightened up their sheep security, Eli and Mary getting shotgun duty. There's even evidence that Tallak ran his logging camps from Idlewild. Ellen was probably chief cook and lodging manager.

But even in this new wilderness, even with her increasing responsibilities, Ellen's future looked good.

She was done with having babies. Done, over, never again. Once Lizzie was weaned her body was her own, creakier than her young years but wiser. The Idlewild homestead had been cleared over ten years ago by the Sawyers and improved over the years — suggesting a more comfortable dwelling than their Sugar Creek shanty. The boys, Tellif and Melvin, were often away; life without teenage boys is always saner. Mary, growing from age twelve to eighteen in the 1860s, could be trusted to do almost everything Ellen did, and Christine wasn't far behind. The older sisters would teach Lizzie to create the tiny, even stitches for mending frocks and trousers and to properly can her first batch of tomatoes. Oscar, the tagalong boy child, would inherit his older brother's chores as Eli graduated to join the men of the family.

Just as steamboats were slowly replacing sailboats on Green Bay waters and portable engines became available for saw mills, new household conveniences promised happiness for the housewife. Surely the treadle sewing machine had arrived in Ellen's sewing space

Now Doty's washing machine ($14) and clothes wringer ($9) was regularly advertised in the newspaper.

. . . Notice the gentle manner in which it handles the clothes, contrast it with the rubbing and scrubbing of clothes on the washboard . . . The Doty's Machine will save the price of itself in the wear of clothes in six months, and will last many years.

Yes; Every Family should have this Washer!

The sewing and washing machines eased the chores of crafting clothing, bedding and linens and keeping it clean for this family of nine. But Ellen sewed by the light of candle or oil lamp, and carried the water from the well to the washing machine throughout her life.

The air she breathed stayed pure and her night sky was filled with stars from forever ago.

Chapter 24 — 1865 – Deeds and Deeds

The *Door County Advocate* was still the only newspaper in the county and the news came slowly. News was delivered by courier from Green Bay — the roads were crucial. In early April the *Advocate* complained: "the late gale has played the Old Harry with our mail, completely blocking up the roads." Finally in the April 20 weekly issue came the news that General Lee surrendered to Lt. General Grant on April 9, 1865.

GLORIOUS
THE REBELLION DEAD
LEE'S ARMY SURRENDERS.
Grant Stipulates the Terms

In the same April 20 issue, but in small print at the bottom of a column, was a dispatch from E.M. Stanton, Secretary of War, dated April 15:

> *Assassination of President Lincoln and Sec'y Seward*
>
> *Abraham Lincoln died this morning at 22 minutes after 6 oclock.*

Following the announcement of President Lincoln's death was a second dispatch confirming the death of Secretary Seward at 9:30. That error was corrected a week later. Secretary Seward was severely injured but did not die.

The war officially ended by proclamation on May 9, 1865.

The number of dead is estimated from 620,000 to over 800,000, two-thirds by disease.

****

The long war was ended, and war spending cuts were immediate, heralding a national depression for the country. The *Advocate* news reflected some Sturgeon Bay problems. Another mill failure was reported when Clark's grist mill shut down in Sturgeon Bay. Farmers had to go to Gardner's mill in Little Sturgeon "with their grists." [Grist: grain that has been separated from its chaff in preparation for grinding.] Mr. Gardner seemed to be weathering the storm, and his general store, sawmill and grist mill advertisement remained the only full column ad in the *Advocate*. The lumber business in Sturgeon Bay continued to thrive, however, with ship arrivals numbering five in one week; one propeller, three schooners and one brig, arriving with supplies and leaving loaded with lumber headed south for the railroads of Green Bay or north around the tip of the peninsula and then south on Lake Michigan to Chicago.

If lumber was thriving, Tallak and Ellen were doing well. Tallak was buying land in the area south of Idlewild, even venturing northeast of Sturgeon Bay to Sevastopol, while selling off all the Big Creek property. A busy man.

****

"No photos, no scanning, no pens. Pencils in the cup by the birth indexes."

I sighed, thinking of my iPhone camera and portable scanner sitting in my backpack.

This was the Register of Deeds for Door County in downtown Sturgeon Bay. I had sacrificed a beautiful summer day to search for the proof of recorded deeds to confirm Tallak's Sturgeon Bay and Idlewild land purchases.

The County Clerk had obviously dealt with many genealogists searching for clues about their ancestors. Her spiel rolled off her tongue before I had a chance to get a question in.

"Back wall holds indexes listing the grantor and grantee of every type of deed or mortgage covering property in this county" she announced, pointing to floor to ceiling shelves, each bulging with archaic-looking four-inch-wide volumes with quarter-inch book-board bindings.

"On these counters are birth and death indexes, and the file cabinets hold the original birth and death certificates."

I sat, a bit stunned at the plethora of research opportunities surrounding me. The library table and six chairs surrounding it took up the remainder of space in the room. It was mine for as long as I needed it.

She left me. I got up and examined the index volumes and plunged in.

The shelves had rollers on them which helped some with dragging the first volume, labeled "1857," down from the top shelf. There, on the first "H" page was Tallak Hoen. The marathon began. Simple enough — retrieve the volume, go to the "H" section, run your finger down the handwritten list of names, first the grantees, then grantors. Record the name, date, grantor, grantee, type of deed or mortgage, section, township, range and portion thereof (i.e. NW 1/4 of SE 1/4) and, very important, volume and page number of original deed. I began handwriting each entry in the notebook I had brought for the purpose, but quickly realized my error as the Haine, then Haines name appeared again and again. I pulled out my computer and began a spreadsheet.

This was my first foray into the forest of deeds in Tallak's name. There were more days to be surrendered to this investigation. I found over two hundred transactions in the name of Tallak or Ellen or his children between the years 1857 and 1899 — including State and U.S. Patent Deeds, Swamp Land Patent, Pine Timber, Warranty, Quit-claim, Land Contract and Door County Tax Deeds. The mortgages included Assignments, Satisfactions, Releases, Notice of Lien and Judgments.

The earliest deeds were handwritten, some with a beautiful hand, some unintelligible. Numbers were spelled out, no numerals in the early deeds. The first few years of index listings included the township, range and section, and a complete property description. Later years replaced the description column with "See deed."

Meaning . . . for a property description on later deeds the original document must be reviewed. Those volumes were in a second, larger, room — floor to ceiling shelves on all four walls, and middle counters with shelves below. Warranty Deeds on this wall, Tax deeds under the center counter, mortgages on the back wall. I learned the anomalies and looked up the most puzzling deeds, gathered the additional information I needed: sales price, mortgage data, complete location description, scouring the handwritten masterpieces. But I couldn't resist looking up the earliest deeds for their beauty alone, and had a few copied ($5.00 each) for their ornamental appeal.

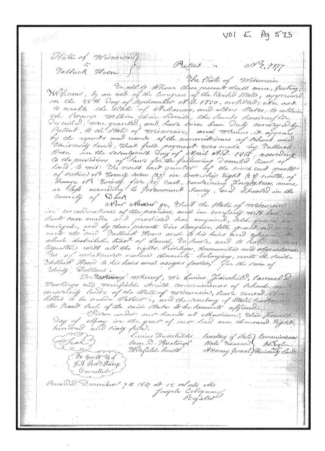

Eventually I spent one full week in 2013, several days in each of the following three years. Next door, at the Land Information Office, I learned how to access the Door County Web Map and search for a parcel using the Section, Township and Range data, then zeroing in on the exact locations on a Door County plat map.

This was tedious work. Happily, the benefits of these searches overcame the pain. Moving dates, family relationships,

occupations, and of course, the financial health of the family —
all come to life in these dead documents. The multiple
transactions among family members when the children came of
age seemed suspicious, as if quick property swaps were a way
to buy more than the law allowed, but I found no regulations that
limited purchases. The land act of 1824 offered lands at public
sale to the highest bidder at a minimum price of $1.25 an acre,
with no limitation on the amount of acreage one individual could
purchase, and no requirement for residence on or cultivation of
the land. I have also found no evidence of a limit on the acreage
or number of transactions for tax delinquent land sales. The
family seemed intent on purchasing as much public land as was
available in Nasawaupee Township, and clearly watched for tax
land sales. Hjalmer Holand chimes in to tell of Tallak's role in
the area around Idlewild:

> *This peninsula [Idlewild] and much more land
> inland was bought by Tallack Haines in 1864. At that
> time the land was wild and he was the only settler in
> a large area. There for many years, he carried on a
> business of cutting logs and hardwood. Usually he
> had a large crew of men working for him (Holand,
> The Old Seaman)*

Ellen began her property activity in 1870, purchasing eighty
acres south of Idlewild for $14.58 on a Door County tax deed.
Then son Tellif picked up eighty acres right next to his mother's
land on a patent deed. In 1871 Tellif bought another one hundred
sixty acres on tax deeds in the same area. That area would be
called Hainesville twenty years later, but it was earning that
name parcel by parcel as the family extended its land holdings
and molded its future.

In the years between Tallak's first Nasawaupee Township
purchases and the calamitous year of 1871, Tallak purchased
over one thousand acres of land in that township. Most of these
acres were virgin forest just south of Idlewild, most purchased

at $1.25 an acre from the U.S. Government — logging this land would certainly require a "large" crew of men. Tallak purchased smaller parcels in the villages of Sturgeon Bay and Bayview. He sold only forty acres in the period. Tallak was holding the land to harvest the valuable timber. Then, when the price was right, Tallak would sell.

Did Tallak and Ellen think of that idyllic Norwegian settlement, of recruiting their Bamble neighbors to come to America and buy and farm some of those Nasawaupee acres? And in Bamble, did Helene and Amund consider emigration, consider attempting to find Helene's family in that foreign land?

During the Civil War, immigration from Europe to the United States had slowed considerably, despite the Homestead Act which Abraham Lincoln signed into law in 1862. The hitch in that act was the necessity to become an American citizen, in a time when that citizenship meant that men between the ages of twenty and forty-five could be drafted into the Civil War. The number of Norwegians emigrating jumped from 1,700 in 1865 to 4,000 in 1866 and continued climbing until the 1880s. But those Norwegian immigrants were not yet storming Sturgeon Bay.

Chapter 25 — 1866 – Gentlewoman and Pioneer

At the homestead in Idlewild, my grandfather Oscar was five, turning six in August. His baby sister Lizzie was three. These were the tag-along kids, the eighth and ninth in birth order. I suspect that Ellen was relaxed in the raising of these last two babies, even counseling Mary and Christine to take it a little easy on their young charges.

****

I was child number four in my family, born seven years after my closest sibling. The parents described by my older sisters were nothing like the parents I remember. My sisters were chastised and advised often. I, hardly ever. I suspect that Oscar and Lizzie benefited and suffered from the same relaxation of oversight. They would inherit the chores ascribed to the younger crew, but not with the same scrutiny or training as applied to their older siblings.

****

Oscar likely bunked with Eli. When Tellif and Melvin were home, now at the advanced ages of eighteen and sixteen, the boys might have crowded together in one bed. Separate beds? No one would have thought of it — there weren't enough quilts and the multiple bodies were needed for warmth. At age six, Oscar was tough enough to endure brotherly abuse from those older boys, with Eli in the forefront. But Eli at twelve was often away with his older brothers now, leaving Oscar the only boy in the household.

He spent his days with the women of the family, his mother and Mary and Christine assigning his chores, and Lizzie his playmate. Their play place? The woods of Idlewild, along with the wolves and the lynx, bears, possums and snakes. These two youngest had their chores. Lizzie took over the traditional introductory job of carrying kindling from woodpile to kitchen, Oscar manned the shovel to clear a winter path to that woodpile, and to the outhouse, barn and chicken coop.

For Oscar and his siblings, the schoolhouse was now far away in Sturgeon Bay, but the emphasis on schooling was building over these years. Tallak's property acquisitions in Sturgeon Bay and Bayview included some habitable houses — Ellen might consider moving into town for a few months, with as many of their brood as could be spared from labor, to get those children some education. Oscar was old enough for the first McGuffey Eclectic Primer, the textbook of the 19th century, published in 1836. His brothers and sisters, no matter what age, began their education with the same book, then graduated to the Pictorial Primer and on to the First Reader. Besides stressing the duties of youth, the stories in the Readers taught honesty, charity, hard work, courage, patriotism, reverence for God, and respect for parents.

When my grandfather turned six in the wilderness of Wisconsin, my grandmother Carrie was born in Norway.

> *I was born in* [Arnesplass] *in Bamble, Norway. The nearest city was Langesund. My birthday: September 7, 1866. My oldest sister died when she was 6 years old so I got her name, Marte Karine. Christian was 2 years older than me.* (Carrie, *My Life*)

As was the custom in Norway, my grandmother Carrie was named Marte Carine after her sister who had died a year before. Marte Carine #1 was named Marte after her paternal grandmother, coincidentally also the name of her maternal grandmother. Now Marte Carine #2 was thrice blessed, with the name of both of her grandmothers and her deceased sister.

From Arnesplass, it was an easy walk for Helene, with Carrie in her arms and Christian walking beside her, to her childhood farm of Vinje where Kari and Lars still lived. Kari was a witness at Carrie's christening in the Bamble Kirke, an indication of a continuing close relationship.

When Carrie was two, her sister Hanna Elise was born. The following year Amund sold their farm at Arnesplass and the family of five moved to the Ødegården farm, purchased for 1,050 speciedalers.

****

My cousin Monica and I drove by the Ødegården farm after we had visited the dramatically situated Arnesplass. The Ødegården farmhouse and outbuildings settled comfortably in the fields surrounding them. No drama here, no fjord at its foot, no multiple rocky levels as their farm at Arnesplass had boasted. But the flat land of Ødegården farm promised better farming potential. This was the home Carrie remembered, where she lived from age three to sixteen. Rogn Beach was within a mile, a lovely retreat for my grandmother as she was growing up.

****

There were many similarities between the communities of Bamble in Norway and Idlewild in America in 1866 — tall pines and hardwoods, large bodies of water playing a crucial role of transportation, livelihoods secured through fishing, hunting and logging, and around every corner beautiful vistas of rocks and water.

But differences, too, were abundant.

In Norway, the original stone church, St. Olav's Kirke, had been built in 1100, the century of Norway's transition to the Christian religion. The new Bamble Kirke was built in 1846, with St. Olav's ruins close by. The church stood in the center of the community, within three miles of any farm, with well-worn paths and wagon trails leading to it. The Bamble parish records document the births, baptisms, confirmations, weddings, deaths and transfers from and to the parish, beginning in 1702.

In Door County, the Moravian church was built in 1864, the first Lutheran church in 1872. Door County parish records began as the churches became established. Distances were long between settlements; it was often a mile or more between homesteads.

The Norwegian Bygdebok, recording farm ownership throughout Norway, began in the mid-1600s. There are two thick volumes for the Bamble area alone. In Door County, the predecessors to the farm where Oscar grew up were the first white settlers, who cleared the land while co-existing with the Indians. The Indian way of life had left the land much as they found it.

In Bamble, all the land that wasn't solid rock had been farmed for centuries. Carrie would walk the two or three miles to the village of Langesund, stopping at her neighbors along the way, on well-worn paths and wagon trails. Oscar, on his seven-mile walk to Sturgeon Bay through deep, dark virgin forest on paths and logging trails created from Indian footpaths, visited only with a Potawatomi family, or a family of deer, avoiding the bear or lynx who might be lurking along the way.

Langesund was established as a municipality in 1838, but its shipyards built ships for Danish-Norwegian noblemen in the early 1700s; records of early Langesund date back to 1664. The town of Sturgeon Bay, Wisconsin didn't exist until 1860.

The difference that towered over all however, was the difference in culture. The people of Norway had evolved in the land of Norway, living similarly, developing conforming traits. Carrie lived with stability, with traditions that were centuries old. The white settlers in America came from many different lands, with differing moralities, languages, building styles, occupations. Each ethnic group did its best to create enclaves mimicking the culture they came from, but to survive they also had to interact with others, learn new languages, and witness if

144

not conform to divergent lifestyles. Door County was truly multi-ethnic with its Germans, Englishmen, Belgians, Irish, Dutch and Native American families. Oscar was raised in this untidy culture.

Twenty-two years in the future, Oscar and Carrie will marry, the marriage of an American-born pioneer with a European-bred gentlewoman. Oscar, never experiencing the European patina, the traditions unquestioned, ceremonies unchanging, and Carrie, never experiencing the early wilderness and isolation of Idlewild or the liberation and loneliness of the missing church community. It would be an interesting marriage.

****

Oscar and Carrie are my maternal grandparents. I lived when they lived. We didn't have many years together; Oscar died when I was six, and Carrie when I was twelve. But I spent the first six months of my life in their home, with my parents and siblings recovering from the poverty of the 1930s depression. When we moved to our own farmhouse, Sunday dinner at Grandma and Grandpa Haines's house was the rule, and we returned home with baskets of vegetables and home-canned goods to augment our still frugal pantry. When I was six years old we moved to the State of Washington, and my grandfather died the following year. "Father passed away suddenly this morning. Funeral Saturday. Don't try to come" said the terse telegram from my Uncle Oliver. We moved back to Chicago after the war, and from age nine to twelve I spent a week or two each summer with my Grandma Carrie and Uncle Oliver on a farm that still had many characteristics of my grandparents' and great-grandparents' lives: no indoor plumbing, no electric lights, no telephone, and neighbors a mile away.

Those short weeks, in those few years, left images and experiences so intense they dominate my memories of childhood. My fleeting taste of the world of my grandparents, my glimpse of the past, sparked my thirst to delve deeper into their world, the thirst that drives the telling of this story.

For those weeks, the stars shone for me as brightly as they had for Ellen.

Chapter 26 — 1867 – Suffrage Delayed

At the time that Ellen left Norway for America, her property and voting rights were nonexistent in both countries. Both Ellen, in Wisconsin, and Helene, in Norway, gained the right to own property, then to control their own earnings, but neither of them had the right to vote in their lifetimes. My grandmother Carrie was thirty-three years old before she was granted the right to vote. My mother was fifteen before the 19th amendment was ratified. My right to vote when I reached the legal age was guaranteed to me at my birth.

****

Did Ellen give it a thought? Did she follow the news of women's suffrage? Did she know that in 1846, the year she and Tallak arrived in America, three hundred activists including Elizabeth Cady Stanton and Lucretia Mott met in Seneca Falls, N.Y. to begin the work to achieve voting rights for women? During the Civil War, suffragists concentrated on the Union war effort, but as the Civil War ended, the debate around reconstruction legislation brought the issue of suffrage for Negroes into the spotlight, and the suffragists grabbed the opportunity to push women's rights into the glow.

President Andrew Johnson stalled reconstruction legislation, but the "Radical Republican" Congress of 1868 successfully revived it. By 1867 the suffrage debate had broadened to include women. In April of that year, the Wisconsin State Legislature, following the lead of other states in the union, proposed an amendment to the State Constitution extending the right of suffrage to women.

Page 1, Column 1 of the July 18, 1867 issue of the *Door County Advocate* announced that the editor of the newspaper opposed the amendment. His editorial filled two columns on that front page. The editorial continued for the next three issues, published weekly — using a minimum of two columns in each issue. It began thus:

> *It is an ugly thing, a hateful task, to discuss any claim of woman in any vigorous spirit. For woman's rights are all that Man can do for their comfort and honor. . .*

> *We object to "woman's Suffrage" then*

The editor went on to express eight reasons, each in amazing detail, to justify his objection. Here I drastically summarize the eight full length columns penned by the editor:

1. She does not have the physical power to fight for her country, therefore she cannot guide its destiny.

2. She is not ordinarily free in political thought because of her devotion to her husband and home —she would vote as her husband votes.

3. She would have to associate with the opposite sex in a free and confidential way to acquire political knowledge.

4. Women by their nature could not forcefully demand anything from the state that her husband brother, father or son wouldn't demand for her every need. Man would feel "grossly aspersed and degraded" by every ballot deposited by a woman.

5. Once women have the vote "they will give themselves office." "One sweet piano YES would trill up from . . . the land." "They will beat us at the polls, as the boys say, 'hollow.'"

6. It will be the most prolific source of domestic discord and suffering ever . . . While men, possessing the full viral-physical force of a genuine political agent, have been protecting women's life and honor, women think only of "shawls, dresses and bonnets . . ."

7. The teachings of the bible are opposed to this . . . "disgusting tendency to a confusion of the occupations of

sexes."

8. Only one in every hundred women have ever thought of female suffrage. "The thing is the monstrous offspring of the few, not the many."

Each column is signed: *Paterfamilias Seipse* [The master himself].

Fitting.

My personal favorite is item 5. Oh, for the trill to sound!

The tirade of this newspaper editor and the many across the state echoing these sentiments convinced the voters (men, of course) to reject the amendment. It was defeated in the Wisconsin State Assembly on March of 1868. (*DCA*, 1868-03-12)

Ellen
Outraged?

What did the women of Nasawaupee Township think? Were they insulted at the weak and shallow depiction of their sex? Where did Ellen, at age fifty-one, stand? Her daughter Mary was fifteen — did she have an opinion? Might the men and women of the family have debated the issue? Did anyone bring it up at some morning coffee get-together of the neighborhood ladies?

WAS ANYONE OUTRAGED?

Forty-four years later, on June 10, 1919, the State of Wisconsin was the first state to ratify the 19th amendment, adopted by the United States on August 18, 1920. Ellen never had the right to vote. Mary was sixty-seven years old when she gained that right.

Norway too was considering the issue of suffrage. When women's suffrage was debated for the first time in the Storting (the supreme legislature of Norway) in 1886, familiar arguments were heard in the hall.

Opponents to women's right to vote argued that it was unnatural for women to have the right to vote, and that it would lead to the disintegration of families and homes. They also expressed the view that "our women should be spared from one of the most difficult dilemmas in life," since it was a man's job to take part in politics. "We do not wish to place this burden on women." And they quoted Bible teachings that women should be kept out of public life.

But in 1898 the Storting adopted universal suffrage for men, allowing non-landholding men to vote for the first time; universal suffrage for women in Norway was adopted in 1913.

Ellen and Helene would have been disenfranchised in either country.

Chapter 27 — 1871 – A Terrible Visitation

Ellen was experiencing the freedom that comes with the final days of child raising. There were no babies in the family. Christine, age thirteen, and even Oscar and Lizzie, eleven and eight, were taking care of themselves and doing their share of the household and farming tasks. Eli was attending school in Sturgeon Bay. His recitation class score — ninety-one percent — and that of each of his classmates, was published prominently in the *Door County Advocate* in June of 1871.

Mary, just eighteen, married Knut Knudson and moved out of the house to a new life. Her older brother Melvin had taken off for Idaho Springs, Colorado, when he turned eighteen, where he worked in the mines for four years. Gold had been discovered in Idaho Springs in 1859 and the town was still booming when he arrived in 1868. He then moved to Golden City, learned photography and opened a gallery. When it didn't work out in Golden City, he tried Denver — but success eluded him. He returned to Wisconsin in 1872. His brother Tellif at age twenty-three was still hanging around the homestead when not logging or hobnobbing in town.

I had assumed that all three of the older boys were following in their father's footsteps in the logging business. I pictured these three boys exactly as an 1870 characterization depicted that breed:

> *"strong and wild in both body and spirit, with the careless masculine beauty of men who live lives in the open air. . . They were magnificent."*

All three fit that description as they were growing up under Tallak's wing — they were required on his logging crew. But after Melvin ran off to Colorado, and Eli took up schooling in town, only Tellif regularly showed up in the woods. A photograph of these three men together, however, displays not

woodsmen, but three magnificent entrepreneurs. Each wearing well-fitted trousers, a vest under the four- button jacket buttoned only with the top button, white collar and tie peeking out above the jacket, and decent looking shoes on their feet. Tellif and Melvin face each other, shaking hands, each sporting a bushy mustache and a bowler hat in hand. Eli stands between them, clean-faced with his hat perched jauntily on his head. He looks on at his elder brothers with the somewhat cynical and all-knowing expression of youth. They are looking more man about town than lumberjack in these poses.

In the summer of 1871, the youngsters and Tellif and Eli were busy fighting the effects of the drought. There had been no rain that summer. It was a summer filled with dust mingled with smoke and ash from multiple small fires starting from smoldering debris left in log clearings, then whipped up by winds and transmitted to wood fences and even outbuildings and farmhouses, appearing spontaneous. The vegetable garden was doing well, thanks to the multiple pails of water lugged by Oscar and Lizzie from well to garden several times each day. The bigger fields of wheat and grain, despite primitive irrigation ditches engineered by the older boys, and multiple water hauls from the nearby bay, were in danger. The three-month drought was unprecedented in this verdant land.

Every issue of the *Door County Advocate* reported on the drought. The dry weather had made the dead timber and leaves like tinder: "Almost every farmer who comes into town has some loss of his property by fire to report" (*DCA*, 1871-09-28 and 10-05).

The logging practices of clearcutting the timber, hauling off only prime logs, then gathering the brush and setting it afire to burn out on its own, were the cause of many fires. Logging had always been done this way, but as homesteads pushed their way into the woods, brush fires spread beyond the forest and found more than logging debris to burn. The settlers built their houses, barns and outbuildings with the most available material — wood — for walls, roof and shingles. The "good" roads were corduroy, made of sand-covered logs. Bridges were fabricated with wood planks supported by wooden timbers and even the sidewalks in town were made of boards. The many sawmills in the area were surrounded by piles of sawdust, and some of its excess was used to pave the streets of the villages.

But even with all that, no one expected the devastation of what came to be known as the Peshtigo Fire.

A Terrible Visitation: An Avalanche of Fire —
Fearful Loss of Human Life:

Over 80 persons burned and suffocated (DCA, 10-
21-1871)

It began at nine o'clock, Sunday night on October 8, 1871:
fifty-seven of eighty residents dead at the Williamson's Shingle
Mill alone — mothers and babies, one old man age eighty-eight,
many in their twenties, and the unidentified: "No. 15. Unknown
Frenchwoman and two children, 1 and 3 y's, no clothes." Then
the long list of wounded, first on the list is Jos. Buckner, both
legs burned off. (*DCA*, 1871-10-12)

Here [Sturgeon Bay] *the night was dark, but*
towards the west and southwest . . . Dense clouds
were noticeable. Then a flame shot up, and the
heavens seemed to be on fire! . . . The terrific roaring
of the wind at a distance, together with the noise of
falling timber caused the stoutest hearts to flutter. The
night was made more hideous by the startling cries of
birds, flying frantically in all directions.

(Chas L. Martin, *History of Door County:* "The
Great Fire")

Chas L. Martin witnessed the fire and its results — his
descriptions are fresh and immediate — and brutal, in the
manner of newspaper reporting of the time. He tells of a scouting
party setting out on Tuesday with mules and supplies for
survivors, but the mules could not continue in the heat and
debris. The men continued to Williamsonville on foot, carrying
what they could:

The journey was dreadful! The odor of wild birds
and animals, together with that of hogs, cattle and
horses that had been roasted alive, mingled with the
dense smoke . . . was almost stifling! Some portions of

*the road were blocked with trees nine feet deep —
burning and smoldering, making the journey both
slow and difficult. Williamsonville was finally
reached — the sight was the most horrible
imaginable! Dead bodies were strewn in all
directions, and most all burned beyond recognition.
Something like thirty-five bodies lay in one heap.*
(Martin, *"The Great Fire,"* 102-105)

Nasewaupee township, including the area not yet called
Hainesville, was "licked up and carried out of existence by the
fire," said Martin.

****

Grandma Carrie tells the fate of Tallak and Ellen:

They lived there [Idlewild] *at the time of the big
fire of 1871. Elias Halvorsen, from Manitowoc, was
there for a visit at the time, and he had a big boat out
on Green Bay so they all went out on that when they
heard the fire howling through the woods. The wind
turned when the fire was about 100 feet from the
house so that was spared . . .* (Carrie, *History*)

The Elias Halverson family had sailed 107 miles from
Manitowoc, north to the tip of the peninsula, then south on
Green Bay to Idlewild. Elias's visit with his wife and six children
was a reason for celebration, an event to bring the old and young
Haines children home to visit with their cousins.

The first thing they noticed that night was the light; it had
grown eerily brighter in the house, brighter than the light of the
oil lamps Ellen had gathered in the big room.

Hjalmer Holand contributes his version of the scene:

[They] *were entertaining themselves with
accordion playing, dancing or playing cards.*

Suddenly Tallack Haines burst into the room and

shouted: "Stop this disorder! Don't you see that death and destruction are over us? . . . the group looked in the direction where Haines was pointing . . . The thick woods, which just a few minutes before had been dark and gloomy outside the walls of the parlor, were now changed to a sea of fire, the flames crackled and wheezed, interspersed with loud crashes, tornado-like — they could see the wild animals running in all directions howling and crying.

Tallack Haines called: "Grab whatever you can and run to the boats. Maybe we can still escape!" They did what he said and ran to the boats which were quickly pushed into the water.

Mr. Holand's description outdoes Grandma Carrie's for excitement — and shouting. Both stories, however, make little of the task of getting from the house to the boat. But winds were recorded up to sixty miles an hour that night, the air was hot, full of smoke and ashes and soot. Burning tree limbs were flying through the air, wild animals were intent on outrunning the fire. The women wore long skirts with multiple petticoats, corsets, perhaps even delicate dancing shoes for this night. Did they have time to change into boots and coats, could they wet down some quilts or rugs to throw over their heads? It was a terrifying flight. There were twenty-seven in all, seventeen in the extended family plus the ten hired men, running to the rocky shore, clambering into rowboats, climbing onto the "big boat," in seas riled by wind and cluttered with burning timber and fleeing, frantic beasts. From the six-year-old to the sixty, it had to be a mad, frantic journey. But they made it, thankful for their unruly refuge, heaving and straining on its anchor. They turned and watched, expecting to see the house go up in flames.

Mr. Holand continues:

But, while they were waiting to see their dear old house burn they became aware that the heavy clouds of choking smoke, . . . now were going the other way. The hurricane fire had reached to about 100 feet from the house; then the wind changed and . . . Tallack Haines' house, built on the northernmost point of the peninsula, was saved. But it was the only one saved for 40 miles southward. The thick forest was destroyed and the little that was left was lying in an impenetrable tangle. The whole Belgian settlement was destroyed, and nearly 300 of Tallak's old neighbors around Sugar Creek had lost their lives.

The family survived. 1,500 to 2,500 people died in the firestorms around them.

Chapter 28 — 1871 – The Peshtigo Fire

The family and the family home were spared. But it was a long night in their floating sanctuary. The men were kept busy with their boat hooks to protect the oars from the sizzling-hot tree limbs, parts blown off houses and barns and boats. The searing heat of the early hours diminished, and at around 3:00am rain began to fall, gentle but continuous, cooling the burning coals and dousing the fires. Cooling the family as well, as the temperature dropped below forty degrees in their refuge on the still roiling waters. As the family waited and watched they wondered what had survived this maelstrom.

The rain continued to fall as the dawn broke. Their long, cold, harrowing night was over, but what awaited them? Did their barn and outbuildings survive the night? Their cows, wandering free in the woods as was the way in that time, did they survive?

Historic maps illustrating the burned-over areas include the entire Idlewild Peninsula; there is no indication of the miracle that saved Tallak and Ellen's home. Tallak's land included the northernmost point of the Idlewild peninsula; it is conceivable that only this small triangle of land was spared from the fire. Wild and domestic animals whose bodies weren't strewn in the nearby char might easily have invaded this narrow haven. Bears, lynx, deer, turkeys, raccoons, porcupines, skunks, snakes, mingling restlessly with the domestic horses, dogs, cows, pigs. The house was saved, but one hundred feet from the house — the length of two boxcars placed end to end — the land was ravaged by fire.

The morning light brought the image of their land to their eyes. Was it safe enough for Tallak, his elder sons and work crew, to row to shore to examine the property spared from the fire and get some idea of the damage to the homestead? I'm assuming that this large a party had grabbed several boats, and with the morning sun Tallak and his boys went ashore in the smaller boats with the hired men to check things out. Elias with another man or two stayed with his boat, starting out at first light to sail to the village of Sturgeon Bay, taking his own family and the Haines women, Ellen, Christine and Lizzie. If there was a safe pathway through the sizzling debris and panic-stricken animals, Tallak and his sons might gather clothes and supplies to take to Sturgeon Bay. They loaded what they could into the boats, then followed Elias, rowing or sailing as fast as they could to catch up. Even in the dim rainy light both parties could see the destruction of the land to the south, the land called "the swamp." A week later the *Door County Advocate* would describe the damage:

> *The terrible tornado swept the timber in a swamp west of Sturgeon Bay so that a person is enabled to see a distance of seven miles. The roads are completely blocked. Parties commenced to chop out the road Thursday morning. Until this task is completed, no mails can be transported. At points of the road fallen timber is piled to the heights of 50 feet.* (*DCA*, 1871-10-19)

As the family stepped onto the dock in Sturgeon Bay on this Monday morning, chaos met them. The village had been spared from the fire, but refugees from Nasawaupee and Gardner were streaming in, telling tales of death and destruction. Williamsonville survivors had arrived with horrible stories to tell. Most were walking, some few had horses. The Haines family knew this town well, owned property here. They had a place to stay. But as they walked to their refuge, treading carefully on the slimy wet ash, avoiding the skittish horses, they recognized their Nasawaupee neighbors among the straggling survivors walking by.

Realization of the horrors experienced by families living less than a mile south of them slowly sank in. Their own search for rest might need to expand to include these less fortunate friends.

The tough facts were published a week later: thirty-five families from Nasawaupee burned out, three dead. Burned out: losing house and contents, barn, harvested crops, crops in the field, livestock, tools, even threshing machines. Gardner, Union, Brussels, Forestville and Clay Banks townships were also severely scorched; some people saved themselves by digging holes deep into the earth and crawling in.

The following week's news brought stories from the town of Peshtigo on the west side of Green Bay — 325 bodies buried so far. Expect up to 500, with more dead in Menakaunee and Sugar Bush.

Gov. Fairchild at Green Bay appealed to the people of Wisconsin for aid, for

> . . . *food, bedding, clothing, feed for their cattle, shelter. Flour, salt, and cured meats NOT COOKED, blankets, bedding, stoves, baled hay, building materials, lights, farming implements and tools, boots, shoes and clothing for men, women and children, log chains, nails, glass and house trimmings . . . everything needed by a farming community that has lost everything, . . . (DCA, 1871-10-19)*

News of the concurrent Chicago fire took over the front page that day; twenty thousand houses burned, two hundred people dead, dollar losses estimated at two million dollars. Aid poured in quickly for the Chicago tragedy. The world knew of the Chicago fire within hours of its happening. That city's telegraph wires were intact, and multiple news reporters were on hand to spread the news. (DCA, 1871-11-19)

Telegraph poles no longer existed in Peshtigo and southern Door County, all burned to the ground. News of the scope of the local Sunday tragedy didn't reach Green Bay until late Tuesday. Doctors, nurses and medical supplies reached Peshtigo on

Wednesday, and slowly spread to the surrounding areas. The fire had totally consumed the town of Peshtigo; it and the surrounding villages lost over a thousand people. *Wikipedia* today lists the fire as the deadliest in American history, killing twelve hundred to twenty-five hundred people, we don't even know how many.

The tallies for Door County included 117 deaths, 167 families burned out completely, an additional 200 families lost fences and lumber and some crops. 2 mills, 2 boarding houses, 6 school buildings, 3 stores, 2 saloons, 148 dwelling houses and the same number of barns were destroyed.

Their lives were forever changed, those who lived through the great fire. Survivors told of the whirlwind of flame, great clouds from above the tops of trees, which fell upon and enveloped everything. People inhaled the intensely hot air and fell down dead. Fish were killed in the streams. People thought it was the Last Day. (*DCA*,1871-10-26)

My generation heard nothing of this event from our parents, or our grandparents. You would think that Ellen and Tallak, and particularly their children, would share the story of their close encounter with tragedy. But survivors didn't talk of it. The horror was too deep, too awful. Tallak and Ellen knew that their story was trifling compared to their neighbors; their good fortune an embarrassment.

The Peshtigo and Chicago fires burned simultaneously with three separate Michigan fires: the Huron fires in Eastern Michigan burned forty square miles and killed over fifty people; the city of Holland in Southwestern Michigan was destroyed with two hundred ten homes, ninety businesses, churches, hotels and boats lost, but only one death; in Northwestern Michigan the Manistee fire left over one thousand people homeless, destroyed over two thousand square miles of forest land, and killed two hundred people.

That's five separate catastrophic fires, all on one Sunday evening in 1871. The causes of these concurrent fires have been studied by scientists and scholars over the years. The comet Biela II flew through the sky that night, and some scientists have proposed that Biella was responsible for the multiple fires by spreading comet gas which then burst into flames. The theory was discounted by most people at that time and today. The extraterrestrial theory didn't get much traction, and most believe that the extreme drought condition in all of the fire locations, the continuing practices of the logging industry to leave their debris fires to burn out on their own, the dry timber, and the weather conditions of the night were enough to explain the outbreak.

Increase A. Latham, Door County pioneer, had complained to the Wisconsin Legislature at least four years before the Peshtigo Fire about the careless and wasteful methods of harvesting forest resources in the state's timberlands. That warning voice was ignored, but after the Peshtigo Fire, both government and industry began taking note of their practices. Eventually, over decades, came improved forestry, fire-preventive measures, conservation of natural resources and regulations.

Grimmer lessons were gleaned by the American and British military during World War II. After studying the "Peshtigo Paradigm" — the wind, topography and fire that generated the 1871 firestorm — they recreated those elements for the fire bombings of German and Japanese cities.

Chapter 29 — 1872 – Recovery

In Nasawaupee township, despite Chas. Martin's early observation that it was "licked up and carried out of existence by the fire," roads were soon cleared, the mail run between Green Bay and Sturgeon Bay was restored, and the survivors of the fire returned to their land to salvage what they could. The acres that Tallak, Ellen and Tellif had purchased for logging had no standing timber left to log. By November, however, sawmills were offering "reasonable rates" to buy the stumpage on the damaged lands. The *Advocate* also reported that the mill companies would purchase pine trees killed by the fire if the trees were salvaged in the winter logging season. (*DCA*, 1871-11-02)

Tallak and sons and crew wasted no time in town in October. I can imagine the Idlewild house acting as headquarters for their salvaging operation in that winter of 1871-72, and Tallak hiring on extra men to haul salvaged stumps and trees to whatever market existed.

But that headquarters would be the first to need clearing attention — the house damaged by flying debris and invasion by the homeless forest folk. The land around the salvaged home was strewn not only with collapsed outbuildings and charred timber, but the malodorous carcasses of wildlife and livestock, the stench announcing their presence and accelerating the clearing process.

Ellen and the younger children would be much better off remaining in Sturgeon Bay. In fact, Ellen and her youngest probably had been spending the school months in town before the fire. The village of Sturgeon Bay had built its first public school on the northwest corner of Fifth Avenue and Michigan Street in 1870. With Eli excelling in recitation, I suspect that

Christine, Oscar and Lizzie were enrolled as well. And now, with the devastation of the Idlewild homestead, Ellen planned a more permanent stay, allowing all the younger children to benefit from the schooling available. Before the great fire, Ellen and her brood returned to Idlewild when the school session was done, with interim trips home for holidays and special events (as when Ellen's brother Elias visited on the night of the fire).

At about this time Sturgeon Bay was described by travelers from the city of Green Bay:

> *a pretty village of about 1000 inhabitants, mostly Germans. It contains three taverns, three saw mills, one grist mill, one brewery, two meat markets, two shoe shops, one tailor shop, one English newspaper and various other branches of business.* (*DCA*, 1870-07-21)

> *After a visit to the local brewery, the travelers added that they had never drunk a better quality beer.*

Once the scramble to salvage whatever possible was completed, what next? The residents of southern Door County had made their living from logging. They cleared the land for their family-sustaining farms, a house and barn, garden and crops enough for family and livestock. But they didn't consider themselves farmers. Their livelihood came from logging, making shingles, running sawmills, transporting lumber. Those jobs were gone in this burned-up land.

These were hardy, practical survivors. Now all their land had been cleared with "a terrible efficiency" by the fire, and these loggers and shingle-makers were left with acres of tillable soil. The people knew how to farm to feed their family. It took only three years for the residents to switch to full time farming, raising stock and crops not only for their own needs but for the market. Many were trying out dairy farming and cheese factories began to replace the sawmills and shingle mills. The sawmills didn't vanish from Door County — the forests north of Sturgeon Bay were not touched by the firestorm, and logging continued for many years to the north.

Tallak was a lumberjack, perhaps a minor league lumber baron, a horse trader, a land speculator. He was not a farmer. His Hainesville property had been purchased for logging, its classification as a cedar swamp not conveying the image of good farmland. But his neighbors, starting over on their own swampland, were expanding their crops, trying different grains and their yields were promising. And so, after reaping what lumber he could from his land, Tallak and his crew of sons and hired men kept on clearing. And buying. They sold a few forties, but continued buying both government and private land in Hainesville.

****

The name Hainesville has come up several times in this story, but it is not clear when that name became common. It wasn't until 1888 that the newspapers of Door County used that name when describing the upper half of Nasawaupee Township. Hainesville was neither a village nor town, but a community with a strong identity with the Haines family. Tallak and his children lived, farmed, and at one time or another owned nearly every acre of property in that area. Today the Hainesville Lutheran Church sits in the middle of the community on County M Road and the Hainesville Cemetery is perched on top of the hill on Hainesville Road. Up until about 1950 there was a Hainesville one-room school, and back in Tallak's time there was the Hainesville post office. If you Google "Hainesville, Wisconsin" today, nothing shows up, but if you Google "Hainesville Cemetery" it puts you smack-dab in the middle of this place called Hainesville. Obviously my knowledge of this history is a benefit of my twenty-first century perch — so we shall take the advantage of my prescient vision and proclaim it

Hainesville before its time.

****

Tallak sold just a couple of Hainesville forty-acre parcels and one eighty in the 1870s. The area wasn't a pretty sight. Dismal was the word, treeless from Green Bay shores to the Sturgeon Bay harbor. The settlers would have to buy logs or lumber to build their houses, barns, fences and outbuildings, and then they must farm to make a living, plowing up acres not yet proven as good farming land. The savvy buyer might suspect undiscovered stumps lurking underground, might hear of the innumerable stones waiting to break the blades of the plow. Norwegian immigration was increasing, but sales in burned-out Nasewaupee Township were not going well.

But Tallak and his family continued to purchase land in the area. The goal was no longer lumber, although there may have been some trees left to salvage. Tallak and his crew became proficient at clearing the land, readying it for crops and homesteads. That old dream of a Norwegian settlement, dormant for so many years, may have taken hold again, inspired by Tallak and Ellen but now contemplated by the extended family.

The conversation must have come around to Tallak and Ellen's old neighbors in Bamble. The Norwegians might see this land, despite its current condition, as a ticket to a future better than any they could have in Norway. Tallak remembered his own struggles years ago, and now the new immigrants were telling him that farming in Norway was getting even more perilous each year. Not only was the soil wearing out in the old country, the farms continued to be divided for heirs — less land for each to farm. Young people no longer accepted the centuries-old customs of remaining on the same farm, continuing in the same traditions. They were moving into urban areas, looking for different jobs. But many were looking to America to start anew.

Ellen heard these stories too, and thought of her sister Helene.

Did she have children who were scheming to leave the nest? Did she have children? It had been almost thirty years since Tallak and Ellen had left Norway, left Helene behind. Ellen saw the ads in the *Advocate* and *Expositor* touting cheap ocean steamship crossings and encouraging the new Americans to arrange passage for their old-country relatives. Did Ellen, now sixty years old, encourage her family in a scheme to reconnect with those Bamble neighbors, to reconnect to her youngest sister, Helene?

Chapter 30 — 1872 – Carrie and her Family

When Carrie was six years old, the dreaded scarlet fever hit her family. Everyone was sick, and Carrie's four-year-old sister Hannah died of the sickness. Her brother Christian was ten and Halvor, just one year. Carrie was now the only girl in the family. Her memory of her sister's death is a grim tale to our ears:

When I was six years old we all had scarlet fever. Then my other sister died. The first that I can remember is when father told us: 'If you want to see Hannah die you must look now.' Her eyes looked straight up. Halvor was the baby. Five years later Eli was born so that was our family. (Carrie, *My Life*)

****

My own brother Dickie died of scarlet fever when I was five. He was eleven, my closest sibling, and his death is one of my first memories, just as Hannah's death was to Carrie. Dickie was taken to the hospital, no children allowed to visit, and then he just didn't come home. And we didn't say his name any more. Death is hard no matter how it is experienced; maybe it was harder for Carrie, first named after a deceased sister she never met, then witnessing her sister Hannah's death so starkly. But we, in 1943, turned the other way, erasing my brother from our lives. I wish we could have celebrated his name, not buried it.

****

When Carrie was ten her brother Eli was born. Planned or not, Helene and Amund avoided the norm of a new baby every two years. Helene had borne six children in seventeen years, four were living.

Carrie made the best of her life without sisters.

We had a nice little home in Norway and I can't thank God enough for the good times I had there. Father read the Bible for us every day and took us to church quite often. He sang for us every day, too. Halvor and I watched cows in the pasture in the summertime. I had my knitting with me too. We didn't always like it but it was good for us. (Carrie, *My Life*)

I don't know if the Rogn "summertime pasture" was considered a saeter in the usual sense, translated as a rough pasture on higher land, accessible and verdant only in the summertime. If so, Carrie and Halvor, with help from their father Amund and big brother Christian, herded the goats, sheep and cows to the spring-rich pasture land, with provisions for the two-month stay. Traditionally the eldest daughter and "an attendant or herd boy" spent the summer with the herd. Carrie and Halvor certainly fit that description, with Christian trekking up weekly to replenish supplies. There might be a rough hut for sleeping, and another for sheltering the animals in bad weather. Samuel Becket in his book *The Fjords and Folk of Norway*, published in 1915, describes the saeter as the domain of women, a lonely life, but the young women of Norway became accustomed to it and "suffered from a curious longing for the quiet of the solitary saeters and brisk mountain air."

When summer was over, if Carrie and her brothers attended school, it would be the "folkeskol" in the neighborhood with a roving teacher. They finished school at age fourteen, earning their confirmation rites in the Bamble Kirke. Schooling still wasn't mandatory, but some schooling was necessary for confirmation, and remember, the confirmation certificate was required before a marriage could be performed.

Carrie recalls:

I was confirmed in Norway. I can't remember much of what Pastor Lampe told us but I intended to live a Christian life. I liked to go to prayer meetings but there was always a fear over me all the time.

I kept on praying God to let me live until I could go to communion again. I thought that would help take that fear away. It didn't go but one evening at the prayer at our house there was an old man standing by the door talking about his experience and faith. Just then my fear was taken away and I could say with the Salvation Army "the burden rolled away". I seemed to see Christ on the cross for a second. I had much trial and fear since but not only fear. (Carrie, *My Life*)

The deaths of her two sisters, the threat of scarlet fever and other diseases, witnessing her parents worry about food on the table . . . the fear is understandable. All of Norway continued to experience years of drought, inadequate harvests, hunger. The family knew of their neighbors who had made the decision to emigrate to America. Perhaps this family too, was thinking of the solution of emigration. The seeds of discontent were planted. What would it take for this family to make the decision to leave their Norway?

Chapter 31 — 1875 – Growing Older

Civilization was coming along in greater Door County.

A short distance from Sturgeon Bay, the ship canal operations were proceeding apace. "The dredge has worked its way well up into the marsh, . . . and forty-four men and twenty-five teams are at work on the cut." (*DCA,* 1872-08-22)

Besides the Moravian and Catholic churches in Sturgeon Bay, the Tanum Lutheran Church was organized in Clay Banks in 1872, about sixteen miles southeast of Idlewild, eventually with a traveling pastor who reached out into the more distant homesteads.

By 1874, Tellif and Melvin were exploring their own urban adventures. Tellif at age twenty-six became a candidate for Sturgeon Bay Town Supervisor in April. Unfortunately, he came in fifth; only the top three were elected. (*DCA,*1874-04-09)

At about the same time Melvin, twenty-four, recently back from Colorado, opened a store in Bay View, selling groceries and dry goods, boots

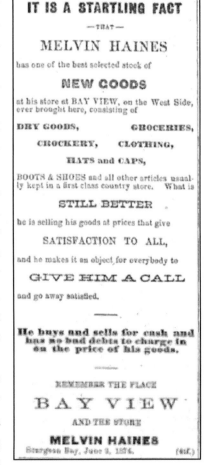

and shoes. (*DCA,* 1874-07-30) Melvin's biography states that Tellif was his partner in this venture, but the Door County

Advocate never mentions such an association.

Melvin married Mary Sorenson in November of that same year:

> *That wedding dance and supper given by MELVIN HAINES and wife, in his building over Bay View last Friday night, was a success from every point of view. And if anybody went away dissatisfied with the manner in which they were received and treated by Mr. and Mrs. MELVIN, they ought to be kicked to death by butterflys. The dancing was kept up until between four and five o'clock in the morning and all were merry as a marriage bell. (DCA, 1874-11-12)*

The dancing turned to dust as the 1875 nationwide depression reached Sturgeon Bay; by January 1875, the store had failed. In one day judgments of over $1,100 were filed against Melvin. Six months later the building was sold in a sheriff's sale, but Melvin was dancing again:

> *The party at MELVIN HAINES place last Monday night, was not as largely attended as it should have been. Those that did go seemed to enjoy themselves- as they kept up the dancing until far into the next morning. (DCA 1875-02-25)*

The Door County Advocate pronounced:

> *We are sorry that the unusual depression business has brought* [the store closing] *about, as Mr. Haines is a man who commands the respect of all who know him. We hope soon to chronicle his re entrance into business. " (DCA, 1875-01-21)*

And sure enough, by 1876 Melvin was on the town board of Nasawaupee Township. *(DCA, 1876-04-07)*

At about the same time, Tallak, nearing sixty-five, sold most if not all his Idlewild property to his son-in-law Knudt Knutson, the husband of his daughter Mary. Tallak and his crew had cleared the land, and the Idlewild property was no longer needed as a logging headquarters. I doubt that Ellen and the children had returned to the Idlewild homestead in the years after the fire. Oscar, Lizzie and Christine were getting the schooling that had been denied the older children — although Tellif, Melvin and Mary must have picked up some learning along the way, as they lived literate lives, managing their farms and business ventures with aplomb.

In 1877, Tallak and his son Tellif went exploring out west. They traveled to Deadwood City, Dakota Territory, by railroad from Chicago to Wisner, Nebraska, with the last 400 miles traversed by horseback or stagecoach.

The gold rush of Deadwood had begun just one year before their arrival and Wild Bill Hickok was killed in Deadwood that same year; Calamity Jane was living in town as Tallak and Tellif rode in. The predominantly male population was there to make a fortune mining for gold, but most of the gold ended up in the pockets of the proprietors of the saloons, gambling establishments, dance halls and brothels in town. On March 7th, 1878, the *Door County Advocate* reports that Tallak "is doing tip top in the gold country."

Tallak returned to Nasawaupee in 1878, leaving his son to the unruly rabble. A year later the *Advocate* reports that Tellif sent a note confirming that he was accumulating some wealth; the newspaper also stated that "Tellief never was worth a copper at boasting." Indeed, the 1880 United States Census lists Tellif living in Arrow Foot of Crows Peak, County of Lawrence, Territory of Dakota. Crows Peak is in the hills about fourteen miles northwest of Deadwood. Census detail lists Tallif as partner to Henry Court, owner, living with thirteen other boarders, all single men, listed as laborers. So Tellif isn't mining gold, but keeping to the lumbering trade, and not as a laborer, but partner to the owner. There were roads to clear, and lumber needed to build the towns springing up around every mine.

History confirms that those who provided services to the gold rushers prospered more than most miners.

Tallak, back in Nasawaupee, was busy:

> *We learn that Mr. Tallak Haines, of the town of Nasewaupee, is erecting one of the best dwellings in the county. His farm is situated near what is known as Sand Bay, between the old Sawyer place and Squaw Island, where he has over one hundred acres cleared up ready for cultivation. Through the enterprise of Mr. H. quite a number of settlers have come into that part of the town, who are clearing up farms, etc. and at no very distant day we expect to see that one of the most flourishing sections of the county. (DCA, 1878-03-21)*

Hjalmer Holand mentions this house too: "Compared to the new settlers' log cabins it was very large, and called *The House* for many years."

We think we know where this house was, we descendants, but while we can identify Squaw Island and Sand Bay, "the old Sawyer place" is puzzling, although it might refer to the Sawyers who sold the Idlewild land to Tallak years before. Was Tallak building that magnificent house for Ellen? The 1880 U.S. Census confirmed that Ellen was living in Nasawaupee Township, age 63, married and keeping house, with Oskar at 19 working on the farm and Elizabeth [Lizzie], 17, "at home". Ellen was a grandmother now, and probably all her energies were focused on Melvin, his wife Mary, and their babies. Melvin and his wife had moved to Hainesville to farm shortly after the store in Bay View had failed.

Ellen's role as grandmother had increased in 1878, as her daughter Christine at age twenty inherited an immediate family when she married Hans Eliason, age thirty-eight. Hans and his family had immigrated from Bamble, but his wife died shortly thereafter and left Hans a widower with two children. Hans purchased a farm in Hainesville at the time of his marriage to Christine — all of Ellen's grandchildren were now living in Hainesville.

Of course Ellen was there too. She would want to be closer to her grandchildren.

It was a hard, hard time for Melvin and his family. Their first child, Ida, born in May of 1877, died within days of her birth. Melvin's second child, Oliver, named after Ellen's "Halvor" who had died in the Civil War, was born thirteen months later, and died of lung fever before his first birthday. (*DCA*, 1879-01-16) Ellen would be grieving with her son in 1878 and 79. And worrying about her daughter-in-law, now in her third pregnancy with a child due in November.

****

My own granddaughter Kaera died of leukemia when she was two years old. I stood by as my son and his wife struggled with weeks in the hospital, then home for a week, then back to the hospital for the next treatment. Kaera's leukemia did not go into remission, treatment decisions mounted: increase dosage? consider bone marrow transplant? experiment? And finally, the hardest decision of all . . . stop. Just stop. My pain seemed multiplied, watching the heartbreak of my son and his wife, and feeling the heartbreak of losing my grandchild, but a grandmother's pain is complex; my son lived, his child died. The grief belonged to him; to claim it for myself felt like trivializing his. In 1879, the death of a child was much more common than in 2012. We suppose, today, that because it was more commonplace, it was easier for the survivors to accept, and their grief was less than we feel today. I disagree. We grieved the same, Ellen and me.

****

Tallak is not listed in the 1880 census with Ellen, Oscar and Lizzie. It could be that Tallak and Ellen were living separately, given the effects of the fire, the emptying nest, and Tallak's meandering around the country.

But in fact, Tallak was not living in Nasawaupee Township nor anywhere in this country. On June 3rd, 1880, Tallak was in Bamble, Norway, enjoying a cup of coffee with Helene.

Chapter 32 — 1880 – Ellen

Tallak, his daughter Mary and her husband Knudt, sailed to Norway in April of 1880, returning in mid-July. (*DCA*, 1880-03-25 and 07-22) Ellen stayed in Hainesville. Why was Ellen not on that boat in April? Of all, she was the most anxious to see her sister Helene again. Mary had never met Helene, and Tallak was merely a brother-in-law.

But Ellen was ill in the early months of 1880; perhaps she asked Mary and her husband Knudt to go in her place. At least Ellen could participate in the planning. Now she would work on getting well, and wait for the news when the trio returned. And maybe, just maybe, Helene would return with them.

Despite my theory of Ellen's preoccupation with the grandchildren, it's hard to imagine it taking precedence over seeing Helene and her homeland once again. The health issue seems the most plausible. But since she did remain in Hainesville, she could enjoy her newest grandchild, Melvin's son Oscar, now six months old. He was a healthy boy, a blessing for this beleaguered family. And Ellen's daughter Christine was expecting her first child in October, to add to Hans's two children from his previous marriage. Yes, Ellen would keep busy with these grandchildren.

The Sturgeon Bay Ship Canal opened for smaller craft sometime in 1880 — and Tallak, Mary and Knudt might have been on one of the first steamers sailing south direct from Sturgeon Bay to Chicago. In Chicago, they traveled by train to New York, then boarded an ocean steamship, still equipped with a few masts for sails when necessary. They disembarked in Liverpool, England, boarded the train to the town of Hull on the eastern coast of England, and finally boarded the steamer headed northeast on the North Sea to the port of Porsgrunn, Norway— the same port where Tallak and Ellen and her mother and siblings had begun their journey to America thirty-four years earlier. No friends or relatives were there as Tallak, Mary and Knut walked down the gangplank — according to my grandmother Carrie they had given no warning that they were coming. The trio hired a carriage and began their two to three-hour ride to Bamble. Not knowing where to find Helene after all these years, Tallak might guide them to Smedplassen, his birthplace, to find a brother or sister to assist them in rediscovering the 1880 Bamble.

Here's my grandmother Carrie in her historian voice:

> *In 1881* [1880], *Tallak, his daughter Mary, and her husband Knut* [Knudt] *Knutson went back to Norway to see how Hellene was getting along. She had not heard a word from them in all those years (35) because no one of them could write. Hellene by this time was married to Amund Rogen and had four children (Christian, Karine, Halvor, and Elias* [Eli]). *He* [Tallak] *had one cousin with him, his daughter. He said they were all living, and had homes and families.* (Carrie, *History*)

And now she can tell the tale in her memoir voice:

> *That was a great day, the day Uncle Tallak came*

to see us in Norway. I, Karine, remember it well as I was 15 years old then. Mother did not know him and he would not tell us who he was. His sister's daughter was at our place visiting just at the time, too. We were afraid of him until he told us that he was Tallak Haines from Amerika. Was it ever wonderful when the questioning began! When Cousin Mary came, there was still more questioning.

After visiting with us, Tallak went over to visit Edwin Grasymr's grandmother. She knew him. Tallak had worked there before he went to Amerika.

When Uncle Tallak, and Mary and Knut went back to "North Amerika" my brother Christian went with them. After that we sure got the fever, too. (Carrie, *My Life*)

Tallak, Mary and Knudt stayed in Norway for three months. Only Christian returned with them, but Tallak had spread the word of magnificent Hainesville among his old friends and neighbors during those weeks in Norway. Not only were Helene and Amund excited about emigrating to America, all Bamble was talking about old man Tallak and his tales of wondrous Door County, Wisconsin.

Ellen was happy to see Christian, and to hear the news about Helene and her husband Amund and their family. And to hear that Helene was coming to America, actually moving with her family to Hainesville. What a joyful reunion that would be! But Ellen hoped they would hurry. Her health had not improved during the three months her husband and daughter had been away. She felt her strength ebbing.

Ellen rejoiced at the first birthday of Oscar, Melvin's first child to live a full year. And Christine had borne a beautiful little boy. But Ellen's health continued downhill. Melvin's child would die at age two. Ellen did not live to see the misery of the death of Melvin's child Oscar. . . nor did she live to see her sister

Helene step off the steamer in Sturgeon Bay.

> *The Last Roll Call: The wife of our esteemed friend and patron Tallak Haines, of Nasewaupee, died at her home in that town early Saturday morning, Nov. 27. Deceased had been afflicted with a cancer on the abdomen for a long time and death was no doubt a happy release from much pain and suffering on earth.*

> *She was sixty-three years of age, about thirty of which had been spent in this country, herself and husband being among the earliest settlers. Six children, all of them grown-up, mourn the loss of a kind and an affectionate mother. Her remains were interred in the Nasewaupee town cemetery last Monday, a large number of friends and neighbors taking part in the last sad rites. (DCA, 1880-12-02)*

They didn't even print her name. Ellen Kristine Halvorsdatter Høen Haine, who sailed three thousand miles over the ocean, traveled another fifteen hundred across America, up the Hudson River to Albany, then across New York State on the Erie Canal to Buffalo, then, bound for Wisconsin, a two-year detour to Canada, finally reaching Port Ulio, Wisconsin, to Green Bay, to Sugar Creek, and Idlewild, traveling by foot and wagon, sailboat and steamboat, living in primitive log houses, fighting fires and wild animals and raising eight children, and putting up with the "esteemed friend and patron" Tallak Haines for thirty-six years. That Ellen. They didn't even print her name.

The newspaper did print the only details known of her death, and I must agree that her death might have been a "happy release." Her medication choices were morphine, laudanum, extract of willow bark and home remedies, including whisky. There were three hospitals in Wisconsin, none of them in Sturgeon Bay, and one was a hospital for the insane. The treatment for cancer was surgery, and as much from lack of hygiene in surgical theaters as from primitive surgical methods, these treatments were seldom successful.

How much her husband Tallak contributed to the pain and suffering on this earth is information beyond my reach. It has always seemed somewhat heartless to his descendants that Ellen's husband and daughter left for Norway just seven months before she died of a "long-term" cancer. But it isn't unreasonable to trust that despite Ellen's inability to travel, she would welcome any chance of seeing Helene again, or even to hear a word of how she was. And despite the newspaper's diagnosis, we don't know how sick Ellen was when her husband and daughter left.

In the end, Ellen was surrounded on her deathbed by her husband and all her children except Tellif, who arrived from the Dakota Territory just a few hours after her death. (*DCA*, 1880-12-02)

Her faith surely included the hope of soon seeing her baby daughter, Gunhild, who died just days after her birth, and her son Halvor, dead at age 17 in the Civil War. Her two long-gone children might be playing with those grandchildren she so recently lost.

But my story of Ellen is done. My attempt to find her in the dense fog of a woman's life in the 19th century, to picture her homes, her furnishings, her daily chores, finished. She would have a chuckle, I'm sure, at my efforts here, puzzled by my lack of understanding of her environment, her rich emotions, the basic elements of her life. "Dig deeper," she would say, "feel how I felt. There was more music, more tears, more love."

Chapter 33 — 1882 – Widower Tallak

Tallak was a widower at sixty-eight years of age. His youngest child, Lizzie, was seventeen years old. The rest of the children were in their twenties and thirties, married or marrying and building their families.

Tellif, the oldest, age thirty-three, managed to court Mary Lavassor in the week following his mother's death, and to marry her ten days after Ellen died, despite his three-year absence in the Dakota Territory. (*WEI,* 1880-12-17)

This *Advocate* article, published just a few days before the wedding, suggests that Tellif had known the family, and Mary, for years. It gives us another look, too, at the everyday hazards that ice, water and animals presented to these early Americans.

> *While crossing from Bay View to this side of the bay with a horse and cutter this Thursday, Tallief* [sic] *Haines and Paul Lavassor met with quite an adventure . . . When partway across, the horse, which was a spirited one, got friskying about and soon got one of its legs over the thills* [Shafts of the sleigh between which the animal is harnessed].

> *This so frightened it that it became unmanageable and capsizing the cutter threw the occupants out and started for this shore on a dead run. Paul, who was driving, clung to the reins and was dragged some distance. He was compelled to let go when he observed the horse leave the regular track and [head] for a large opening in the ice. Into this the animal plunged and the impetus carried it under the ice on the opposite side where it was beyond the reach of help and doubtless shuffled off the mortal coil in less time than it takes to tell. . . The animal was valued at $150* [and] *we are informed that Mr. Haines*

*presented Mr. Lavassor with enough shekels to
replace the loss. Good! (DCA, 1880-12-09)*

Melvin, Tallak's second son, and his wife Mary were
struggling with their multiple losses, as their third child Oscar
fell sick and died in his second year. Mary was pregnant again.

Tallak's oldest daughter Mary and her husband Knudt were
living in Shawano County, Wisconsin, with many ties to
Nasawaupee County, including the fact that they now owned
much of Tallak and Ellen's original Idlewild land. (*DCA,* 1880-
07-22)

Eli, at age 26, will soon move to Woonsocket, Dakota
Territory and marry. But Eli too acquired some of that Idlewild
land.

Christine's first child, Thomas, was born in October 1880.
Thomas would live for just two years. Christine did not have
another child, spending her energy on Hans's two children. It
was a hazardous time for babies.

Oscar, the youngest son in the family, who had been living
and farming at the Haines home farm until Ellen died, joined the
ranks of the magnificent lumberjacks.

*Oscar Haines, who has been logging in the
northern part of the county with his brother the past
winter, returned with his camp equipage last Friday
night. The boys put in about 330,000 feet of pine, with
enough to make half a million feet left in the woods,
which could not be got out on account of the poor
sleighing. (DCA, 1882-03-23)*

Since Oscar had three older brothers, he could have been
logging with Tellif, Melvin or Eli, but perhaps this was the
beginning of Oscar's partnership with Tellif. These two, the
youngest and oldest of the boys, worked together for the next
dozen years.

Finally, Lizzie, the youngest child. Lizzie and Oscar were

living in their mother's home when she died; presumably Tallak was there too. However, Lizzie was the logical caregiver during her mother's illness. Tallak, Oscar and Lizzie called the Big House home, but the men quickly found various adventures that lured them away. Did Lizzie continue to live there? Alone? Who did the farming?

In February 1881, the *Door County Advocate* advises that Tallak "has disposed of his farm and other property in Nasawaupee for $6,000 and distributed the proceeds to his children." (*DCA*, 1881-02-03) Property records corroborate major transfers of property from Tallak to Knudt and Mary, his daughter, smaller transfers to Oscar, along with selling some land in Bay View and Hainesville to third parties. Mary and Knudt in turn transferred property to Mary's siblings, Eli, Tellif and Melvin. Whether sales or gifts is unclear. Hjalmer Holand suggests that Tallak was still interested in selling the Hainesville area to his friends and relatives in Norway:

> *Old Tallack, who had almost lived his three score and ten, thought he could be spared from active work so he decided he should do something to advance the area so it could become what it should be: A good Norwegian settlement.* (Holand, *Hainesville*)

To that end, Tallak signed a power of attorney giving his son Melvin authority to act in his name and in September of 1881 Melvin revealed to the *Advocate* that he had received a letter from his father.

To continue: Melvin received a letter from his father reporting that he was with relatives and friends in Langesund, Norway, a village close to Bamble. Tallak "went away some time ago" said Melvin, but didn't tell his family where he was going. (*DCA*, 1881-09-30) The *Advocate* appeared to be collecting multiple "leaks", as it reported in the Nasawaupee Column that:

Knud Knudson, of Angelica, Shawano county, has been stopping at the Tallack Haines place, in the northern part of this town, for several months. (*DCA*, 1881-12-22)

I suspect that "stopping" means staying there, not just checking on things occasionally, in which event, through no help of the reporters, we assume that Tallak's daughter Mary was also "stopping" with her husband Knudt. Company for Lizzie.

Tallak evidently planned a much longer visit on this trip. Ten years had elapsed since the Peshtigo Fire; the cedars and maples would be a decent height, some over twenty feet. Hainesville looked good again, if not the voluptuous virgin forest of pre-fire years. The Haines family had land to sell, and Tallak's plan was to continue the campaign he had begun on his first trip just a year before: Sell Hainesville to his long-ago neighbors in Bamble.

Helene needed no encouragement. Ever since that earlier trip in 1880, the household of Helene and Amund had been abuzz with the plans of following their son Christian to America.

Carrie tells her own story.

That next year Aunt Ellen Haines died so the next winter Uncle Tallak came back to Norway and stayed over winter. So then my father bought a farm from him in Hainesville, and we sold everything. We had a nice home there in Norway, too. (Carrie, *My Life*)

I wonder how many acres of land Tallak managed to sell, sight unseen, on this trip to Norway? We know he returned to Sturgeon Bay with either eight or twelve immigrants, including the five in Helene's family. I suspect he had sold additional acres to some Bambleingers who were planning a later emigration. Not bad, Tallak.

Helene's emigration experience in 1882 was similar to the journey of her sister Ellen's in 1846, but with some note-worthy differences. Just as Tallak and Ellen had done, Helene and

190

Amund sold their farm, sorted clothing, household goods — this to take, this to leave behind, this for the journey, this for the destination. They were allowed ten cubic feet of space for their luggage, and travel trunks remained the standard shipping container, many beautifully decorated. But on this trip, their food would be provided by the steamship, they need bring only eating utensils, mattresses and personal belongings for the crossing.

Helene must have struggled with the same emotions that Ellen had felt at leaving their country, their family and friends, their traditions. But Helene had lived forty-nine years of her life in Bamble and left her adopted parents, Kari and Lars, in Norway. Ellen left at age twenty-eight, emigrating with her mother, her husband and child, and five siblings. Amund said goodbye to his recently widowed father and four siblings. Ellen's child Halvor, at two years, would not remember his first years in Norway. Helene's children, Christian, age twenty and already in America, Carrie at sixteen, her brothers eleven and eight, were young people with their own ties to school and friends. Helene took comfort in anticipating the reunion with her siblings — but siblings she had not seen for thirty-five years, aunts and uncles and cousins her children had never met, speaking a language new to all of them.

Like Tallak and Ellen, Helene and Amund had the comfort of traveling with some fellow Bambleingers. Perhaps more important, they had the advantage of Tallak's guidance for the journey, not just across the ocean, but to an established settlement, where their son Christian and Helene's siblings and nieces and nephews would welcome them to the new land.

They were going to America.

Chapter 34 — 1882 – Bamble to America

It was far more common in 1882 to witness friends and neighbors leaving Norway — but the departure of Tallak and his sister-in-law and family, together with the three or four additional Bamblingers leaving on that fair May Day might still draw a crowd of relatives and well-wishers. Tallak's brothers and sisters, the Vinjes, Amund's family, and of course, the curious, gathered around to wish them Godspeed.

The emigrants might need to travel to Christiania [Oslo] by land or steamer, to board a ship headed for Liverpool. From there they boarded a steamer headed to the North Sea southwest to the port of Hull, England, 504 nautical miles, taking two to three days. They waited for their train to arrive in the emigrant waiting room of the Paragon Railroad Station, recently doubled in size to accommodate the increased number of migrants taking the train the 126 miles to Liverpool. A tiresome trip — open windows, admitting steam and soot and noise from the locomotives, crowds jostling for space amid a medley of unfamiliar languages.

They would welcome their sleeping quarters in Liverpool. The beds, perhaps even a room, for the interval before their ship arrived were included in the price of the passage. The wait was guaranteed to be no longer than a week. Sometime around the 8th of May they boarded the steamship *Scythia*, 4,500 tons, iron-hulled, single screw with one funnel and three masts, carrying 839 passengers on this crossing, 111 cabin and 728 steerage. Their fellow passengers were from England, Sweden, Wales, Ireland, Scotland, Denmark, France and, yes, a good many from Norway. Ellen and Tallak had traveled with just 92 fellow passengers, all from Telemark, Norway, on the 287-ton sailing ship *Sultan* with three masts, no funnel. In 1846 the crossing took eight weeks. Helene and Amund were at sea for approximately eight days.

On Tuesday, May 16, 1882, the *Scythia* crept into Upper New York Bay, then dropped anchor close to the shore of Staten Island. All passengers were summoned on deck for the routine inspection for signs of contagious diseases. The Boarding Department officer inspected the ship records for illnesses and deaths during the crossing.

On this day, a second boat came alongside and, not routine, a U.S. Marshal with six deputies and the British Consul-General came aboard. They announced that they were searching for "some persons" implicated in the assassination of Lord Frederick Cavendish in Dublin. The Marshal ordered the assembled 839 passengers to split into groups of men and women. The men were put on "dress parade" for their examination. The women, including an anxious Helene and Carrie, were "scrutinized in order that no man may escape by being clad in feminine apparel," in the words of the *New York Times* article. No villain was found. One wonders how the "scrutinizing" was done. (*NYT,* 1882-05-18)

The Marshal, his deputies, and the British Consul-General finally left the ship, the passengers relaxed, and the *Scythia* was allowed to sail on. The rails were packed with relieved passengers as they sailed past Bedloe Island — without a second look — no Statue of Liberty stood high in its center. They might have heard of the grand plans for the statue now being built by Gustave Eiffel, and the torch-bearing arm first displayed at the 1876 Centennial Exposition in Philadelphia and now intriguing New Yorkers in Madison Square Park.

Tallak glanced toward the East River docks, remembering his 1846 arrival and marveling at the Brooklyn Bridge now just beyond those docks, almost ready for its grand opening in 1883.

Now all eyes were focused on the tip of Manhattan where the distinctive Castle Gardens stood, the last hurdle before being accepted into America. Castle Garden Immigration Center, open from 1855 to 1890, was the precursor to Ellis Island, established to protect the immigrants from the rogues and scoundrels who had swindled new arrivals on the open East River docks.

The *Scythia* set anchor again a short distance from Castle Gardens. The Landing Officer handed Amund and Tallak a metal tag matching the tag he attached to each piece of luggage. Bags went one way and passengers another as they transferred from the *Scythia* to the waiting barges. It might take a while to transfer everyone, the 111 first class at the head of the line and the 728 steerage passengers following. Their landing was neither as exciting nor as terrifying as the East River docks had been in 1846, but dry land and the ornate rotunda of Castle Gardens would do as their first look at America. A final health exam, this one not interrupted by the U.S. Marshal, then the registration agents recording the name, nationality, former address and destination of each new arrival. Tallak checked with the railroad agents, arranging the railroad travel from New York to Chicago, then deciding between the steamboat route to Sturgeon Bay or the alternate railroad to Green Bay and steamer from there.

Amund dealt with the money changers. They didn't need the letter writers and labor exchange also provided at Castle Gardens, and with Tallak to guide them would avoid the ever-present hawkers waiting for immigrants just outside the Castle Garden gates — hawking their hotels or transport or murky travel deals to unsuspecting immigrants — shades of 1846.

When all the entry procedures were complete and the luggage retrieved, Helene, Amund, Carrie, Eli and Halvor were free to step out onto the streets of New York, into their new lives in the United States of America. The New York Times reported 6,949 immigrants passing through Castle Garden in the week that Helene and Amund arrived in 1882.

Tallak and his troop might walk behind the luggage wagon directly to the train station, with plenty of company. I've felt the excitement of walking those lower Manhattan streets, Broadway on its slanted route slashing the narrow old streets, the crowds, street vendors, and still the tenements, dirt, noise, chaos. These newcomers to America felt that excitement. Were they exhilarated or terrified?

Trinity Church, dwarfed by skyscrapers on my 2015 visit, was still the tallest structure in Manhattan in 1882. Did they take that slight detour to Madison Square Park to see the preview of the arm and torch of the Statue of Liberty, a closer look than I could have today? Did they climb the stairs to stand in the torch and look over the city of New York?

The streets of lower Manhattan were not so different from the time of Tallak and Ellen. The transportation choices were similar, walking or riding in a horse-drawn carriage — the horse-drawn streetcars were a new addition, but horse manure remained the main pollution problem. My walk in 2015 had different transportation choices — most going no faster than those in 1882 — with a different type of pollution.

The journey that my grandmother Carrie would remember from Bamble, Norway, to their new home in Door County took no longer than three weeks. In fact, there was just one month and a day between the date they recorded their emigration in the Bamble parish *Utflytte* register to the date of their arrival in Sturgeon Bay. It had taken Tallak and Ellen seventeen years of experimenting and exploring before they arrived in Sturgeon Bay. Helene, Amund, Carrie and the boys would marvel at Tallak's stories of the three-month-long journey from New York City to Buffalo in 1846, their two-year detour in Canada, and their final arrival in Port Ulio, Wisconsin.

The Nasawaupee News column in the *Advocate* kept the community informed of Tallak's progress, with the help of Melvin's latest update from his father's letters. In March of 1882 it is reported that "the old gentleman" was homesick, but wouldn't be home before spring because many friends were coming back with him. A few weeks later comes the news that he would be home in April, and finally on May 25:

> *Tallack Haines arrived back home from Norway on Tuesday's boat after an absence of nearly a year. He was accompanied by eight or ten persons who propose to make America their future abiding place.* (DCA, 1882-05-25)

No mention of Tallak's relationship to Helene's family.

Even without Tallak's efforts, some of the Norwegians pouring into America during the 1880's would find their way to Door County. Immigration statistics list 1882 as the peak of Norwegian immigration, with 26,966 Norwegians arriving in America in that year. The Cunard Line offered emigration packages at $19.00 per person, including steamship ocean passage and railroad travel to Chicago, about half of the 1846 passage cost of Tallak and Ellen for their ocean crossing alone.

Carrie tells her short story of the journey and arrival:

In the spring of 1882 we all left for Amerika. There was plenty of sea sickness, too, when that big ocean liner rolled over the waves. But, when we got to the big square house in Hainesville, Mary and Lizzie had everything ready for us. (Carrie, *My Life*)

Helene and family arrived in Sturgeon Bay on May 3, 1882. Their son Christian, and Tallak and Ellen's two daughters, Lizzie and Mary, might meet them at the dock. Tallak and Ellen's youngest son Oscar was in town, just returned from a winter of logging in northern Door County, but probably too busy with his recent land acquisitions to join the welcoming crowd.

But Oscar would meet his new cousin Carrie soon. My grandparents were together in America. All is in order. I am pleased.

Chapter 35 — 1882 – Immigrants Reunion

Carrie, her mother Helene, and their family would feel at home in the Hainesville countryside. Certainly they felt welcome, with Christian to greet them and the hospitality of their American kinfolk.

Christian . . . had rented the Idlewild farm so we moved into that clean little house there. (Carrie, *My Life*)

There might have been several new houses built on the Idlewild farm in the eighteen years that Tallak and Ellen had owned this land. This "clean little house" could be the original house that Tallak and Ellen had lived in, the one saved from the fire in 1871, or a newer house, built from milled timber. Carrie hadn't seen many log houses in Bamble. It is understandable that Norway had abandoned the simple log built homes long ago. The water-powered sawmill was invented in the 1500s and Norway had been exporting boards to many European countries who lacked the wood needed for construction as early as 1700.

But if the homes of Hainesville looked rustic and foreign to Carrie and her family, the waters surrounding the community reminded them of the fjords and the North Sea surrounding their community of Bamble. The land in their new home was just a little wilder, with fewer well-worn paths, fewer neighbors. The surrounding waters were a little milder, the inland fresh-water Green Bay and Sturgeon Bay replacing the salt of the rowdy North Sea arm of the Atlantic Ocean. And, like Bamble, Idlewild was a peaceful place, few roads from town, transportation by boat in summer, sled in winter.

****

There was one more step to welcoming Helene and Amund, Carrie, Chris, Halvor and Eli. Lizzie and Oscar got busy writing letters to all their siblings to announce the arrival of Helene and family in Hainesville. On July 7, 1882, the *Advocate* got wind of a lot of visiting going on for the Haineses, but no mention of a reunion.

> *Jas. Halverson, of St. Croix county, this state, were here last week visiting the Haines. Mr. H. is a brother of the late Mrs. Tallack Haines. Other relatives from Port Washington and Canada were also here at the same time.* (DCA, 1882-07-07)

Carrie tells her story:

> *That summer mother's brothers and sisters came to see her* [Helene]. *Aunt Nellie came from Canada, Aunt Kirsten and family from Port Ulio, Uncle Eli from Manitowoc, Uncle Jens from Star Prairie, Minnesota. I have always said it was the happiest time of our life. Mother asked so many questions about how they had been all that time, and they asked about Norway. I had no care. It was so much fun to see all those American cousins that I could not understand. Oscar was the most interesting. He was sick that summer.* (Carrie, *Happiest*)

Helene's six older siblings were teenagers and young adults when they "left Helene behind in Norway" in 1846. This was their first reunion, although the Wisconsin dwellers had visited back and forth individually over the years. All but two would gather — the missing were Ellen, the oldest, now gone from the earth, and Ole, the second youngest. No explanation for his absence.

All but Nella and Ole were living in Wisconsin, at distances from Sturgeon Bay that we would find negligible in the twenty-first century, but a substantial travel effort in 1882. Elias in Manitowoc and Kirsten in Grafton were closest, and had the advantage of traveling by boat, still the most efficient mode of travel. Elias and his large family could hop on "the Staunch and Speedy Side-Wheel Steamboat Corona" with routes between Manitowoc and Sturgeon Bay leaving daily (except Sunday) at seven a.m. Kirsten and family booked passage on one of the regular Chicago to Green Bay routes, disembarking at the Sturgeon Bay Ship Canal.

Jens and his family lived inland in Star Prairie, Wisconsin, across the Mississippi River from Minneapolis, Minnesota, and three hundred miles from Sturgeon Bay. They would find a rail line close by to take them to Green Bay, then steamboat from there.

Nella journeyed the farthest — over six hundred miles from her home in Sparta, Ontario. She followed the route Ellen and Tallak had traveled in 1850, by steamship through Lake Erie to the St. Clair River to Lake Huron, then around Mackinac Island to Lake Michigan.

The five siblings, including Helene, gathered with spouses and children, those interesting American cousins commingling with the newcomers from Norway, Christian, Carrie, Halvor and Elias. The sisters and brothers recalled some exciting, funny and sad stories from their journey thirty-five years back. Tallak told stories about the early adventures that he and Ellen had experienced, and about their mother, Marte, how she had coped with the journey. Helene relished the stories of Ellen and her life in all the different places they had lived. They all missed Ellen — so recently gone, so strong a force in their immigration story.

Then each might relate their own story, all the happenings since they separated from each other. How had they fared, those fresh-faced youngsters, risking that 1846 emigration?

They were all farmers, owned their homes and land. Three of the four, Elias, Jens and Nella, had servants living with them, usually a husband and wife team. All except Ole and Nella married men or women who were born in Norway, but three of the five lived in communities with few Norwegians. Kirsten and her husband Soren had stayed in Port Ulio (now called Grafton), the landing place, now with few Norwegians, leaving a random collection of Belgians, Prussians, Irishmen and Bavarians. Nella had married a New York born Yankee Quaker refugee from Massachusetts. Their Quaker settlement of Sparta included Scots, English, Irish and German. Nella had one Norwegian friend in the nearby town of London, Ontario.

Nella might have news of Ole, who lived in Port Huron, Michigan. Census data reveals an Ole Halvorsen streetcar operator in Port Huron in 1880, born in Norway, married to an Irish woman with a four-year-old with a different last name, and a grandparent with the same name as the child. Maybe streetcar operator Ole wasn't interested in hobnobbing with his affluent siblings. His Port Huron neighbors were a cosmopolitan mix of Irish, English, Canadian, Scottish and Prussian.

****

Migrants all of them. Tallak and Ellen and her siblings were representative of thousands, most clinging to their heritage as they farmed — but raising American children, and blending, despite their efforts to cluster. Some gathered with their countrymen for a generation or two, like Elias and Jens; others were thrown into a hodgepodge of nationalities by choice or happenstance, like Nella, Kirsten and Ole. Tallak and Ellen had prospered in communities of diverse nationalities, and it's hard to know if Tallak's efforts in gathering his Bamble neighbors to Hainesville were for the purpose of building a Norwegian community or to pull off a masterful sales promotion of the Door County properties that he and his family had acquired over the last twenty-five years.

He did both. The Hainesville area remained primarily populated with Norwegians for about fifty years. "They shut out others." said Hjalmer Holand in his Skandinaven article, but scattered Swedes, Germans, even New York Yankees muddied the Norwegian sanctuary from the start. They all slowly learned English as their common language — they traded in Sturgeon Bay, negotiated land purchases with neighbors, sold their butter to Heinrich. They created a beautiful, peaceful rural community; shared with each other, and the larger community. The Norwegian majority slowly dwindled, as their children married "others" and their neighbors sold to any old highest bidder. They built America. They blended. We blend today — same way — by getting to know one another. By realizing the benefits the variety of cultures contribute to our American character.

****

I would think the reunion would last a week or so. They had come a long way. Nella might linger the longest, the hungriest of the siblings for family stories and Norwegian smells. This was her only journey to Wisconsin.

Carrie mentions "all the young folks" — cousins! Except for Carrie and her brothers, all first-generation Americans or Canadians. Cousins, many meeting for the first time, discovering the eerie cousin familiarity with each other as they meet. Carrie remembers:

> There was just one little unhappy moment when I saw all the young folks out for a boat ride and only me left. But then I heard something and there on the shore was [Oscar] who was left too. So we visited, had a plate lunch and watched the sail boat out on Green Bay. No care, just happy. Beautiful sunshine. I didn't know then that this cousin would be my husband. (Carrie, *Happiest*)

And so they met. My grandmother Carrie and grandfather Oscar. Carrie was sixteen years old and Oscar, twenty-two. Not time for a romance yet. But Carrie, at age 80, entitled her remembrance of that day "The Happiest Day."

Chapter 36 — 1883 – Romance for the Old

Romance was in the air for the young . . . and the old.

One week after the reunion, Tallak traveled with Elias as he and his family returned to their home in Manitowoc. "Tallak and his son went to Manitowoc to visit friends." states the *Weekly Expositor Independent* (1882-07-07), the newest news source in Sturgeon Bay. Five months later, January 1, 1883, the *Advocate* picks up the story:

> *Tallack Haines, who intended to spend the winter at Manitowoc, returned here several weeks ago. He thinks there is no place like home after all.*

In April, we hear that Tallak "now occupies the O.S Johnson place, which he recently purchased." (*DCA*, 1883-04-12)

Two weeks later, the *Advocate* scores a scoop:

> *Nasewaupee Column: It will no doubt be a genuine surprise to many of his friends in this town and elsewhere when they learn that Tallak Haines has once again committed matrimony, but such is nevertheless the case. And what is still more remarkable the ceremony took place on the first of last December, and has been kept a profound secret ever since. The bride was formerly a Miss Marie Simpson, whose home is in Manitowoc city, where the marriage was performed on the day above named. THE ADVOCATE unites with a host of friends in extending congratulations to Mr. and Mrs. Haines, and it trusts that the union may prove a long, prosperous and happy one. (DCA, 1883-04-26)*

Ellen had been dead for two years. Shock might be a better description than "surprise" at this newspaper announcement.

Had Tallak purchased the O. S. Johnson place in preparation for the new Mrs. Haines to join him?

The bride was the former Mrs. Marie Simpson. Gunhild Maria Isaksdatter Simpson was a widowed mother who had raised her three children on her own for the last twelve years. Emigrating from Bamble, Norway in 1855, she had married Lars Simpson in December of that year. Lars Simonsson Hoen had immigrated from Bamble in 1849. He was the captain of a schooner in 1860 but by 1870 Lars was farming in Manitowoc. In July of 1870, at the age of 41, he died from dropsy [abnormal swelling in the body, often congestive heart failure], leaving his wife a widow with their two children, Isabella, age seven, Lottie, age three, and pregnant with her final child, Laura, born in September of 1870. Their first child, Ananda Mathilda, had died at six months.

When Tallak married Marie Simpson in 1882, he was seventy years old. Marie was forty-nine and two of her children were still at home, Laura, age nineteen and Matilda [Lotte], thirteen. Isabella was twenty-one and out on her own.

I discovered this second marriage through the research of a fellow genealogist, a descendant of Tallak's brother-in-law Elias Halvorsen. He had hired a genealogist in Norway to research his ancestors and shared the results with me. Listed in the travel records of Tallak Høen was the information that Tallak had a marriage (1) to Ellen and then a marriage (2) to Laura Simpson. I thought it was a mistake. But when I asked a contemporary cousin about it, he said his father had told him that Tallak had married someone in Manitowoc after Ellen had died.

Family lore placed this marriage in the category of "a one-night stand." Carrie never mentions Tallak's second marriage. The new Mrs. Haines is referred to as "Mrs. Simpson" by Tallak's descendants. The *Advocate*, however, assumed the new Mrs. Tallak Haines was the real article, as on July 26, 1883:

Isabella and Lotta Simpson, daughters of Mrs. Tallak Haines, are visiting their parents here. Their home is in Manitowoc.

Yes, there was a new Mrs. Tallak Haines, and "parents" is plural. Tallak not only has a wife, but brand-new children. Laura was not along on this visit. Curious that "Their home is in Manitowoc." Were Lottie and Laura in boarding school there? Living with Isabella? Or perhaps there was an aunt or uncle in Manitowoc who was caring for them. Sources for this part of the story are glimpsed only from public records and newspaper gossip in the Nasawaupee Column. There is not much to go on.

Tallak appears to be continuing in the usual homestead chores, with the *Advocate* reporting on his mishaps:

About three weeks ago Tallak Haines, Nasewaupee, received a kick from one of his horses while engaged about the stable, and although no bones were broken Mr. Haines was quite severely injured. He is just able to be about once more and that is all. (DCA, 1884-02-28)

In 1885, Isabella, Marie's oldest daughter, became a Sturgeon Bay resident through marriage.

There was a marriage in the Moravian church, this city, last Tuesday afternoon by which Nicolais Nelson and Miss Isabella Simpson were united in wedlock. The bride is a step-daughter of Tallok Haines, of Nasewaupee, and up to within a short time a resident of Manitowoc. (DCA, 1885-01-01)

No mention of who attended this ceremony, but Isabella's association with Tallak is there, to the exclusion, one might notice, of any mention of her mother who raised her.

I think our family legend was warped a bit, perhaps by Tallak's children, preferring the more traditional story of Tallak remaining a faithful widower of Ellen, and not messing up the family tree. But Marie and her children became part of the community. Tallak and Marie clearly lived together and Lottie and Laura joined them from time to time. But we will hear more about these newlyweds. The Tallak and Marie saga is not over.

Chapter 37 — 1883 – Family Upheaval

Oscar and Carrie's relationship took much longer to percolate and mature. Carrie, at sixteen, was young for courting. Around the time of their first meeting on the Idlewild shore, Oscar was rapidly acquiring land in Hainesville — he paid $120 for his first property purchase, at barely twenty years old — eighty acres located at the foot of the Idlewild peninsula where he grew up. A year later he purchased thirty-nine acres just east of his first purchase on a swamp-land patent deed. But in August of 1882, his siblings Mary, Elias and Melvin all transferred acreage to Oscar, all in Hainesville, most of them 40 acre parcels but some 120s from Mary. Why? Oscar was property-rich at twenty-two years old.

The puzzle becomes clearer in a lengthy article entitled: "The Good Time has Come" in the *Independent* newspaper the following March, extolling the value of the new Haines Brothers organization set up to purchase hay and produce from Door County farmers. The article notes the great advantage to Door County farmers to have a local outlet for surplus products. The Menominee warehouse expedites the Haines Brothers sales of products that the "northern country" cannot produce for itself. Melvin manages the warehouse business in Sturgeon Bay and Menominee; Oscar attends to the purchase and pressing of hay, charging eight dollars to buy and press on the farm, and nine if the hay is delivered to the warehouse in town.

The article reports that the Haines Brothers harvested fifty-eight tons of hay and fifteen hundred bushels of oats from their one hundred seventy-five acres under cultivation, which they increase annually, having four to five hundred acres in their homestead. "They pay more taxes than any other person in their town, and are unquestionably among the most progressive and enlightened farmers in the state." This Haines Brothers enterprise appears to be a family affair, with the consolidation of acreage in Oscar's name a part of the business plan. (*IND*, 1882-03-16)

Tellif wasn't involved in the Haines Brothers enterprise at its beginning. He announced that he and his family intended to leave Wisconsin around the middle of August for New Tacoma, Washington Territory, "with a view to making that country their home." (*DCA*,1883-05-03)

Eli had already left Door County, had "packed his grip-sack" a year earlier for the "kingdom of Dakota." (*WEI*, 1882-07-21) He put his property, three hundred acres under cultivation south of Idlewild, up for sale "at a bargain." (*DCA*, 1882-08-17) Seven months later, in February 1883, the *Weekly Expositor Independent* reports that Eli has "joined the army of benedict's in that land of prairies and blizzards" and now has a butcher shop and a wife. "Elias [Eli] is an enterprising young man — full of days work. . . He knows how to take advantage of the situation and profit by it."

Tallak and Ellen's original Idlewild land, now owned by their daughter Mary, her husband Knudt and Ellen's brother Elias, was about to change character as well. The rocky shores of the Idlewild Peninsula posed a hazard to the larger steamships now turning into Sturgeon Bay to take advantage of the time-saving ship canal. The Sturgeon Bay and Lake Michigan Ship Canal and Harbor Co. petitioned to condemn one acre on Idlewild's northernmost shore of Green Bay, plus a right-of-way for a road to the shore of Sawyer's Harbor. (*DCA*,1882-05-25). Plans had been drawn to construct the Sherwood Point Lighthouse, with a boat house and coal shed, accessible from Green Bay and Sawyer's Harbor.

Mary, Knudt and Elias were summoned to appear on May 29, 1882 to present their estimate of the land value and the effect on their adjoining land. Negotiations may not have gone smoothly with Mary and Elias. Congress had appropriated

$12,000 for the construction of the lighthouse in March of 1881, but construction didn't start until May 1883 "because of problems securing clear title to the land." Hopefully Amund, Helene, Carrie and the boys had moved out of their Idlewild house to their home in Hainesville before the blasting began.

The lighthouse continues in operation today. It was automated in 1983, one hundred years after its construction; until then it had the distinction of being the last manned lighthouse on the Great Lakes.

Tellif had planned to do his own exploration to check out New Tacoma, but he was feeling the pressure of married life. His wife Mayme was not a strong woman, and now there was the baby under a year old. Tellif had spent the winter logging, and Mayme was tired of his absences. Tellif's siblings, Oscar and Lizzie, footloose and family free, were the perfect substitutes to venture to the west.

I had to dredge that fact that Lizzie accompanied Oscar on this great adventure from the final newspaper article reporting on the trip — Oscar's sister wasn't acknowledged as his travel companion until the couple returned to Sturgeon Bay.

And so Oscar sold his farm, "a part of the old homestead" (*DCA*, 1883-04-26) to his sister and brother-in-law, Mary and Knudt Knudtson, and was ready to take off with Lizzie, just turned twenty, for the West.

****

There was a nationwide recession in 1882-85, and although the Door County newspapers reveal no serious financial reversals in the Sturgeon Bay area, times were hard. The trees that were destroyed by the 1871 fire were growing back in southern Nasawaupee, but the old-growth forests were dwindling in all of northern Wisconsin. Melvin had recently traveled to faraway Drummond Island on the Canadian border with a logging survey team. (*DCA*, 1882-05-25)

The recession might be affecting the Haines family, but all this talk, and action, aimed at traveling and relocating was occurring in the same time frame as Ellen's death, Helene's arrival from Norway, the family reunion, and Tallak's marriage to Maria. Coincidence? I don't think so. Change was in the air, the family seemed to be experiencing growing pains. Tallak's offspring also took after their father, wired to keep moving on, try a new landscape. They were spreading their wings.

Chapter 38 — 1883 – Oscar and Lizzie on the Road

New Tacoma was a hot topic in 1883. Not only were the forests uncut in the Washington Territory, but the Northern Pacific Railroad had announced in 1873 that Tacoma would be their western terminus. They built a depot just two miles from the existing village and called the spot "New Tacoma." By 1884 old and new were merged and became Tacoma again. The railroad arrived in 1887. The population of Tacoma grew from 1,098 in 1880 to 36,006 in 1890.

Oscar carried his proceeds from the sale of his farm in a money belt worn close to his heart — gold coins, some silver, a few gold certificates (Greenbacks). San Francisco, a necessary stop on the route to Tacoma, accepted only gold coins, even silver was discounted. They would learn that fact from their copy of *Appleton's General Guide to the United States and Canada with Railway Maps, Plans of Cities, and Illustrations,* published in 1881.

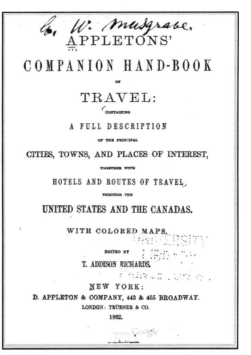

Co. W: Musgrave.
APPLETONS'

COMPANION HAND-BOOK
OF

TRAVEL:
CONTAINING

A FULL DESCRIPTION
OF THE PRINCIPAL
CITIES, TOWNS, AND PLACES OF INTEREST,
TOGETHER WITH
HOTELS AND ROUTES OF TRAVEL,
THROUGH THE
UNITED STATES AND THE CANADAS.

WITH COLORED MAPS,

EDITED BY
T. ADDISON RICHARDS.

NEW YORK:
D. APPLETON & COMPANY, 443 & 455 BROADWAY.
LONDON: TRÜBNER & CO.
1882.

I found my copy online in the HathiTrust Digital Library — it informed my description of the westbound journey for my grandfather and great-aunt.

They packed lightly, heeding the Appleton's Guide advice that sudden temperature changes were to be expected, and that "woolen underwear should be worn both summer and winter, and a shawl or extra wrap should always be at hand." Surely Tellif, at least, came to see them off, feeling melancholy at being left behind.

Lizzie and Oscar probably reached Chicago in mid-May of 1883, either by steamer to Green Bay and rail to Chicago, or steamer on Lake Michigan direct from Sturgeon Bay. From Chicago it was rail-rail-rail. They bought their train tickets, about $15.00 each, for the first leg of their journey from Chicago to Omaha. They chose one of three railroads, Chicago, Burlington & Quincy; Chicago, Rock Island; and Pacific, or Chicago and Northwestern. Each line had two through trains daily, each with the same accommodations and each traveling five hundred miles to Omaha, on only slightly different routes. Oscar and Lizzie surely opted for the Pullman Palace sleeper car at an extra $2.00 to $3.00 per day. The trains traveled an average thirty miles per hour, with many stops. It took at least one day and night to travel those five hundred miles, maybe two.

They traveled through Illinois and Iowa, then crossed the Missouri River into Nebraska at Council Bluffs and arrived in Omaha. The land remained familiar on this leg of the trip, mostly rolling hills and farms and forests.

They found beauty and bustle in the city of Omaha. It was the largest city in Nebraska, with 30,500 inhabitants, and, as Appleton's Guide described "Its streets are broad, cross each other at right angles, and are lighted with gas." — all quite upscale.

But on the second leg of this journey the hills were about to morph into a land unknown to Oscar and Lizzie. A 2017 check of Google maps calculates the driving distance between Omaha and San Francisco at 1,665 miles. The Union Pacific Railroad to Ogden, together with the Utah and Central Pacific from Ogden to San Francisco, logged 1,916 miles, according to the Appleton Guide.

The fare was one hundred dollars, plus eight dollars for the Pullman Palace from Omaha to Ogden, Utah, and six dollars from Ogden to San Francisco (the approximate equivalent in 2013 is $2,200 for the ticket, $300 for the Pullman Palace add-on.) Travel didn't come cheap in 1883.

"No more fruitful outlay could be made" touted our guidebook in praise of the Pullman Palace options:

> *THE journey from Omaha to San Francisco, . . . is more like a sea-voyage than the ordinary rushing from point to point by rail, and . . . one ceases to care about time-tables and connections, and makes himself comfortable.*

The guide then quotes a pamphlet called "California, for Health, Pleasure, and Residence:"

> *Until you have undertaken this journey, you will never know how great a difference it makes to your comfort whether your train goes at the rate of 40 or at 22 miles an hour. . . At 40 or 45 miles per hour, the country you pass through is a blur; one hardly sees between the telegraph-poles; pleasure and ease are alike out of the question; reading tires your eyes, writing is impossible, conversation impracticable . . .*

> *But, at 22 miles per hour, travel by rail is a different affair; and having unpacked your books, and unstrapped your wraps, in your Pullman . . . Palace-car, you may pursue all the sedentary avocations and amusements of a parlor at home . . . your dinner is sure to be abundant, very tolerably cooked, and not hurried; . . . and as the country through which you pass is strange, and abounds in curious and interesting sights . . . you soon fall into the ways of the voyage;*

At that relaxing pace of twenty-two miles per hour, the 1,916 miles from Omaha to San Francisco took four and a half days.

Oscar and Lizzie had their faces glued to the window, marveling at the wide-open prairie, no trees, no stumps, the land changing from farming to grazing country, stretching out to horizons difficult to grasp. They glimpsed herds of grazing antelopes, and prairie-dogs standing at attention. They might have jumped off the train at the Sidney, Nebraska, stop, the closest to the new home of their brother Eli in Woonsocket, Dakota Territory. Then, shortly after Sidney, Oscar and Lizzie caught their first glimpse of the Rocky Mountains.

They were headed into this breathtaking land on a formidable conveyance. In the next few days, the locomotive(s) hooted through fifteen tunnels, conquered gradients of up to 116 feet per mile, dared tight turns with precipices yawning on one side or the other and risked rickety wooden bridges spanning canyons of beauty and depth unimagined by my grandfather and his baby sister.

****

I remember my first view of the Rockies. I too was traveling from Sturgeon Bay, Wisconsin to Tacoma, Washington. My journey west was sixty-one years after Oscar and Lizzie made the trip — my father at the wheel of our 1937 Ford. I, at six years old, was allowed to sit in the front seat between Mom and Dad, inhaling the excitement of my father as he negotiated the tunnels, tight turns, precipices and gradients of the 1944 highway. We stopped at every pull-off with its welcome water spout to fill up our radiator and replenish our bumper-mounted canvas water bag. The bridges we crossed were less rickety than in 1883, but the beauty they spanned as unbelievable to us as it was to Oscar and Lizzie.

We knew little more of this land than my grandfather had before setting out on this journey. We both had heard stories and read articles of earlier travelers, and my family had seen photographs in National Geographic, a source not yet available for Oscar and Lizzie. Movies, in the 1940s, were not included in my family's depression-recovering budget, and TV, though invented, wasn't a household item. We were virgins traversing this splendid land of the west, both generations blessed to experience the unsullied, unexploited beauty.

My father had a job waiting at the Bremerton Navy Yard in Washington, sixty miles north of Tacoma, allowing us special wartime gas rationing to make the trip. We were also driving away from my brother's death. My mother was subdued, her body tense when the road hung on the edge of a mountain. My two teenage sisters in the back seat were a team, frenemies, but two. I was twin with my dad, anticipating, scanning, my dad always the first to call out "deer," "elk," "moose" along the road. But we did not anticipate the ruggedness, the awesomeness of these majestic mountains and waterfalls, canyons and cliffs. We were as spellbound as Oscar and Lizzie had been on their 1883 adventure.

Chapter 39 — 1883 – Travels of Discontent

Oscar and Lizzie's westward train ride ended at the Oakland, California dock, where a ferry carried them across the Bay to San Francisco. That city was rich with hotels, restaurants, theaters and reading rooms. Telegraph Hill, Golden Gate Park (no bridge), the Cliff House, the University of California at Berkeley, two medical schools, many hospitals and asylums. San Francisco too boasted "broad streets that cross each other at right angles" plus a lively China Town of 20,000 Chinese.

> *Tallief Haines received a letter from his brother Oscar, who left here several weeks ago for Washington Territory. The epistle is dated San Francisco, which place Oscar describes as a pretty dirty-looking city and numbering among her inhabitants about 40,000 Chinamen. He had never seen a "heathen Chinee" before reaching the west, and it is safe to say that the young man was not very favorably impressed with those people. Tallief will join his brother as soon as the latter strikes a favorable location. (DCA, 1883-06-14)*

The "Chinee" were there to build the railroad. They came to work in the gold mines in 1850, then moved to agriculture, the garment industry and finally became the major source of cheap railroad labor. But now the railroads were almost completed, and anti-Chinese sentiment was rising. The Chinese Exclusion Act was adopted in 1882, the first legislation in American history to place broad restrictions on immigration. The restrictions were renewed ten years later, then indefinitely.

The Chinese were our allies during WWII. The restrictions on Chinese immigration were repealed in 1943.

After their evaluation of San Francisco, Lizzie and Oscar

headed for their primary assignment, to check out New Tacoma.

Back in Sturgeon Bay, the *Advocate* offered their editorial opinion about that city, not waiting for the latest report from Oscar:

> *New Tacoma, Washington Territory, to which place several Door county people intend to go, is said to be overrun with emigrants. Many of them are unable to find work, and are consequently subsisting on short rations.* (*DCA*,1883-06-14)

Image ID: 55098
View of New Tacoma and Mount Rainier, Puget Sound, Washington Territory. (1878)

Steamboats ran daily from San Francisco to Tacoma, but Appleton's Guide recommended the interior route to New Tacoma "for a better view of the countryside": first re-trace the railroad trail to Sacramento, from there catch the Oregon rail line to the Columbia River, then enjoy a steamboat interlude on the Columbia to Kalama, Oregon Territory, and finally board the Oregon railroad to New Tacoma.

However they got there, the Advocate reports on July 5th that Oscar was unimpressed:

Oscar Haines is still prospecting out west. He traveled through Washington Territory, but the country didn't suit him. . . At last accounts Mr. Haines was in Deer Lodge, Montana, which he describes in a letter to his relatives here as a dull place. Unless he finds a desirable locality in Montana very soon he will go to Texas.

But our travelers didn't make it to Texas. Lizzie and Oscar headed to Deer Lodge, Montana, via a collage of rail, river steamboats and stagecoach. The route was circuitous, south to the Columbia River, rounding the Bitterroot Range of the Rockies through Boise, Pocatello, then straight north to Deer Lodge. The Northern Pacific western advance reached Deer Lodge by around July of 1883, just in time for Oscar and Lizzie's return trip. They were one summer early for the Northern Pacific Railroad's push through Stampede Pass, heading straight north towards Tacoma. One summer early to experience the four standard time zones implemented to simplify train travel. Just a few summers early for the imminent demise of steamboat and stagecoach travel.

****

My sister and I were many summers late to experience the railroad depot at Deer Lodge, on our tour through that area in 2015. We were late to experience the Northern Pacific Golden Spike in Gold Creek — where the railroad crews from the east and the west met in August of 1883 — but in 2015 the town no longer existed and the roadside history turnoff celebrating it was closed for repair. The Northern Pacific no longer ran passenger trains through Stampede Pass and there is no paved highway through the Pass. We sped through the Cascade Mountains on highway 90 east and west of the historic route. Too late.

***

Oscar and Lizzie were on their way home when the *Advocate* announced that Tellif was no longer interested:

> *Tellief Haines has about decided to remain here. His brother Oscar, who has been prospecting out in Oregon and Washington territory for several months, is very much dissatisfied with that country and advises him (Tallief) not to come out as he has thus far been unable to find a suitable location. It is probable that Oscar will return here soon.* (DCA,1883-07-26)

Perhaps all those negative reports were the result of travel fatigue; nothing is satisfying Oscar. We don't hear Lizzie's opinion, of course, but perhaps even Oscar's opinions were begin filtered through the viewpoint of the editor of the *Door County Advocate*.

As we remember from the spirited essay dismissing the idea of women's suffrage, the editor of the *Door County Advocate* was a man of strong opinions, which appeared regularly on the pages of his newspaper. There had been many vigorous editorials encouraging the residents of Door County to ignore the current propaganda touting the lands to the west. Stick it out here in the Midwest —your home,

I have not discovered a single letter between Tellif and Oscar to back up the negative press reports. The story written in those letters must have discouraged Tellif from changing his residence, but even a dullard would be excited at the ruggedness, the awesomeness of the western land, the exotic animals and the harrowing route of the railroad trains. No man or woman, of that century or this one, could fail to be impressed with the City of San Francisco, its setting, its sophistication. I suggest a slight skewing of emphasis to complaints over exaltation. Oscar and Lizzie are offspring of Tallak — they had a great time.

By August they were home again, making plans for their future in Hainesville:

> *Oscar Haines and his sister, who have been sojourning out west for some time past, are expected home this week and will probably remain permanently. It is reported that Oscar and his brother Tellif will enter into co-partnership and engage in the purchase and pressing of hay at Bay View. THE ADVOCATE hopes the report may be verified. (DCA, 1883-08-09)*

As I mentioned earlier, I sneaked Lizzie's name into this story at the beginning. Only the final article above mentions that Oscar's sister (no name, just "sister") was traveling with him the whole time. Tellif will stay in Door County for now and join the Haines Brothers in their fall harvesting season.

Tellif will hear the call to the road again. I understand that call. I inherited it.

Chapter 40 — 1884 – Church, Hay, Sorrow

While Oscar and Lizzie were sojourning out west, Carrie was busy arranging the plank pews in a vacant storefront for the first official worship service of the Sawyer Norwegian Lutheran Church.

My grandmother Carrie wrote down her memories of that first service:

> *I remember the first service that was held in a small building near Frank Larson's. N.N. Anderson went up in the morning and swept up. Then they carried in some new planks for us to sit on. I do not remember what the pulpit was like--a table I think. Rev. Magelsan* [sic] *from Manitowoc was the pastor.*
> (Carrie, *Church*)

It was fall of 1883 when Reverend Claus F. Magelssen, from Bergen, Norway, proclaimed the Gospel from the table serving as a pulpit. The eight founding families savored the familiar liturgy, singing their Norwegian hymns from memory, feeling home seep into their lonesome bones. After that first service, there might be a second one in a few weeks, or months. Rev. Magelssen served the congregations of Sawyer, Manitowoc and Tanum, spending many hours on horseback, wagon or sleigh visiting remote farmhouses, but was not expected to hold services every week.

Carrie's father, Amund Rogn and Oscar's father, Tallak "Hain," both attended the organizational meeting, along with nine other men, many from Hainesville. Tallak's son Melvin joined the group at its second organizational meeting. Tallak retained his reputation as a leader in the community, despite whatever gossip emerged about his marital choice.

It was no surprise to see Amund Rogn among the organizers.

He and his family were newly arrived from Norway, anxious for a continuation of their traditions. Amund and his fresh fellow immigrants had never lived in a place without a church, the Bamble Kirke steeple standing tall in their lives. These new immigrants had baptized their babies, confirmed their youth and sanctified their marriages in the church and buried their elders and their children, in the cemetery next door, with every rite recorded in the parish records.

Tallak organizing a church? Not so easy to understand. It's true that Tallak and Ellen had dipped into church whenever the proper church was in the neighborhood — that being both Norwegian and Lutheran. Halvor had been baptized in Bamble and Tellif was belatedly baptized in Port Ulio, with Melvin, Mary and Elias following him as they came along. But there was no baptism for Christine, Oscar and Lizzie, despite the Methodist, Catholic, German Methodist-Episcopal, Seventh Day Adventist, Congregational, and the Norwegian Moravian Lutheran (with both "Norwegian" and "Lutheran" in its name) all available in Door County. Did Tallak catch a whiff of nostalgia, remembering his and Ellen's names recorded in the Bamble Parish, from their baptisms to their marriage, so long ago?

Oscar and Tellif, those unchurched country-cousins, were not a part of this church organizing zeal. Immediately on Oscar's return to Hainesville, the Haines Brothers enterprise pops back into newspaper prominence. Their letterhead states their purpose:

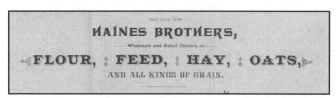

The Advocate reports on their newest farm machine August 23, 1883:

Oscar Haines returned from Chicago this week with a new hay press, and the machine is now at work on his father's place in that town, [Nasawaupee] where . . . one hundred tons of hay will be pressed. . . farmers who desire his [Oscar's] services can obtain them at very low rates. The machine makes only small bundles, they being more in demand among purchasers than packages of 300 and 500 pounds.

And reports their progress in September:

On Friday last a ton of hay was pressed in the short space of an hour with Oscar and Tellef Haines hay-press. As it usually takes two hours to do that amount of work, this must be considered good time . . .

They had a bunch of hay days ahead of them. It was a new idea, putting hay in bales. Haystacks were the old way of storing hay, then moving the loose hay into the haymow in the winter, fork by fork. This hay press was on wheels, an improvement over the stationary press powered by dropping a weight from the second story of the barn to press the hay.

"Haines Brothers" become a brand, appearing repeatedly in the *Door County Advocate*:

The Haines Bros have taken a contract to press 50 tons of hay for Joseph Smith on the latter's farm in the town of Jacksonport . . . The Messrs. Haines have purchased another press in order to keep up with their orders. (DCA, 1883-10-04)

Melvin's name doesn't appear often in the multiple newspaper reports of the Haines Brothers activities, but the organization seems flexible, with the three resident sons alternating their involvement as demands of the business and demands of their own homestead fluctuate. The business plan was simple, with the brothers buying and pressing hay for the farmers, then selling elsewhere, mostly in Menominee. They were transporting their goods using barges and ships based in Sturgeon Bay — although they continued to haul their own loads in the winter over the ice.

The brothers purchased a plow in 1884, "the largest ever brought to this county." Intended for breaking ground heavy with brush, it cost the company $35 to $40 and required two to three yoke of cattle [oxen?] to operate.

Oscar and Tellif had worked together since 1882, when Oscar, age twenty-two, spent the winter logging with Tellif, a veteran lumberjack at thirty-five. Thirteen-year age difference between those two, and ten years between Melvin and Oscar. Oscar is the baby of the business — but he seems to be the one constant in this family enterprise that continues through the next ten to fifteen years.

The winter of 1885-86 tested the symbiotic partnership, putting the greater burden on Oscar to manage the Haines Brothers business, as Tellif focused on the health of his wife.

> *Mrs. Tellef Haines returned here with her husband last week, having been unsuccessful in procuring any medical aid for herself either at Milwaukee or Chicago, and her case is pronounced a hopeless one. Consumption is said to be the cause of the trouble.* (DCA, 1885-07-02)

Her condition did not improve, even after Tellif moved his family into Sturgeon Bay to be closer to medical help, hiring a man to care for their farm. Mary Lavassor Haines died at age twenty-six on November 15, 1885. Two daughters, Ella age three, Mary Edna, almost one, survived her. Less than one month later, Mary Edna died. (DCA, 1885-12-10)

Consumption, today known as tuberculosis, took both mother and daughter.

Chapter 41 — 1886 – Death and Travel

The winter of 1886 continued to be a tragic time for the Haines family. On December 30, Mary Haines Knudtson's husband Knudt died. The death of Melvin's wife Mary followed six months later, shortly after the birth of her sixth child. Her first three children had died before they reached age two. Her last three were four, two and an infant when she died. She was thirty years old. This death could have been caused by consumption . . . or simply sorrow and exhaustion.

Tallak's three oldest children had buried their spouses in one year, his two sons struggled with babies all under four and his daughter was navigating widowhood at age thirty with no children. I assume that Tallak, patriarch of the family, father-in-law and grandfather of the deceased, would attend the multiple funeral services, if able, with the new Mrs. Tallak Haines on his arm.

However, both might have been preoccupied with attending to Tallak, as yet another injury has prompted the *Advocate* to alert its readers that Mr. Haines's injuries might "shorten his days":

> *Tallack Haines is still suffering from the effects of an accident that befel him about two months ago, and it is feared that he cannot fully recover owing to the infirmities of age, he being within a few months of seventy-four years old.*
>
> *The accident . . . was caused by the running away of Mr. Haines team of horses during which he was thrown out of the wagon and severely injured about the body, though fortunately no internal harm was inflicted. Mr. Haines is one of the oldest residents of Door county, . . . His many friends will regret to hear*

that an accident has befallen him which may very materially shorten his days . . . (DCA, 1886-09-09)

Tallak paid no attention to the prediction.

But in March of 1886 Tellif came close to being another family casualty on the job. He was working with Oscar, operating a logging camp in Egg Harbor, about seventeen miles north of Sturgeon Bay. They had partly loaded a sled with logs. Tellif had just hooked up a fresh team of cattle to pull the log on the skids to the top of the load. He had been using a slower team which gave him time to get out of the space between the logs and the team after he gave the start order. The new team moved the log more quickly than Tellif expected and he was caught between the advancing log and those already loaded:

> *He commanded the oxen to stop, but they refused to obey him until the log was almost upon the sled, at which time the head of Mr. Haines was caught between the logs and was somewhat hurt. Had the team advanced another inch the skull of the young man must have been crushed, as there was not the least chance for him to extricate himself. (DCA,1886-03-11)*

Logging was a brutal occupation. But they got this job done quickly — the camp broke up two weeks after the terrifying incident. It was a two-month operation in which 216,000 feet of logs "were banked [stacked on the shore of a river or lake] on a three-mile haul," considered a success for the number of men and teams. That was the end of operations in Egg Harbor "as about every available pine tree has been cut and hauled." (*DCA*, 1886-03-25)

Three months later we hear that Tellif is "compelled by failing health . . . to leave for Spearfish, Dakota Territory, in a few days." It was not surprising that Tellif was feeling low — this man has just gone through several years of anxiety and hopelessness for his wife's health, then her death, and one month later, the death of his one year old daughter. Thank goodness young Lizzie has stepped forward to help him with his daughter Ella, not quite four years old. "His sister Lizzie and his child will remain here until he arranges for their reception, and will then follow him to the west." (*DCA*, 1880-06-03)

Tellif had traveled to the Dakota Territory for the first time in 1877 when "he was obliged to travel by stage three hundred miles from the nearest railroad station" to reach Deadwood; in 1886, the railroad stopped just ninety miles out of Deadwood and soon the railroad would reach that city. (*DCA*, 1886-06-03)

On July 16 *The Independent* reports that "Miss Eliza Haines leaves for Deadwood D.T. where her brother Tellif resides . . . Mr. Haines little daughter will accompany her."

Lots of excitement for a four-year-old — and for Lizzie as she assumes this role of nanny for her niece and travels to the Dakota Territory once again.

Oscar stayed behind and carried the load of the Haines Brothers business in the fall of 1886, including traveling to Menominee for several days at a time to tend to business matters. (*DCA*, 1886-09-16)

> *Oscar Haines has pressed fifty tons of hay during the past few weeks and one-half of this amount has been purchased by parties in Menominee, who paid sixteen dollars a ton therefor.* (*DCA*,1886-09-09)

Tellif was exploring the opportunities in the Dakota Territory. He was working for a lumber company and noted that the common laborer was paid thirty to forty dollars a month, a rate expected to decrease as "the tide of emigration continues." Tellif is skeptical about the idea of speculating in the mines, "there are as many losers as gainers." He described Carbonite Camp, a town that grew to half the size of Sturgeon Bay in six months, with mostly cheap structures except for a hotel built with one hundred thousand feet of lumber, costing thirty dollars a thousand.

Tellif did not recommend that anyone follow him to Dakota, "everything being uncertain." (*DCA*, 1886-09-02)

Carbonite Camp was a good illustration of that uncertainty. The camp was named after carbonate ore, a mixture of silver and lead discovered in 1881. It boomed for two years, sagged when the mines were closed, sprang back two years later when a nearby gold mine prospered. The hotel that Tellif described was the William Hugginson's Black Hills Hotel, the largest in the Dakota Territory in 1886, three stories high with a saloon and banquet room. Two years later a diphtheria epidemic attacked the town, the mines petered out, and by 1900 Carbonite Camp was mostly deserted. In 1901, the Black Hills Hotel was torn down, its lumber salvaged to construct nearby Cleopatra Mill. Carbonate Camp survived for about ten years, William Hugginson's Hotel a mere five. Today the Camp is an official Ghost Town, with only rusting mining equipment remaining. At least they recycled that lumber!

Oscar worked long days while Tellif was exploring the Dakota Territory. But once the harvests were done, and the hay was transported to buyers in Sturgeon Bay or across the waters in Menominee, Oscar had time on his hands. The snow began falling, Christmas approached, and at-home parties sprang up, gathering the young people for dancing and singalongs, games and a little romancing. As the news of a party somehow spread among the farms, aprons were flung aside, fiddles grabbed, horses hitched to sleds, and the celebration began. Oscar was there. Carrie too. Carrie at twenty — no longer a wide-eyed teenage newcomer. A woman. Oscar noticed.

Chapter 42 — 1887 – Cousins Correspond

So begins our first intimate glimpse into the budding romance between these cousins, my grandfather Oscar and grandmother Carrie. Oscar's words reveal the courtship that was well underway by the time he joined Tellif and Ella in the Dakota Territory.

Sawmill Gulch January 15, 1886

Dear Fraind an Cousin Carrie

I will try to write to you this evening but I do not [know]*what to write as here is nothing but Logs, Hills and mountains but I know you will not write to me til you get a letter from me and I want to hear from you soon*

Lizzie is getting supplies and Tellif has gone to town   he has been to Spearfish since day before yesterday . . . I have worked every day this week we are up at half past four every morning it give me very good epetite to walk up and down Hill all day . . .

It isn't yet the custom to worry much about punctuation, like periods and such. A few words are left out, the spelling is suspect, capitalization seems random and paragraphs nonexistent. My personal grammar anxiety begged for order — the remaining transcriptions are cleaned up a bit.

. . I hope you are feeling better. I hope to find you all right in the Spring and do not forget your Reading you will have a chance to practice on this letter. i cannot read it all myself. I have not had time to get Lonesome yet. Ellen [Ella, Tellif's four-year-old daughter] *is telling me my fortune with cards she says i am going to have a letter but i doubt it. I will commence to look for this in about the last of next week*

I am learning two new songs to sing for you when I get home.

Lizzie had a letter from Elias. [Eli] *he said he would come out here to see us this winter. he can drive across the Prairies with his Ponys. I hope he will come then we will be quite a family.*

Lizzie is talking some of going [to] *Bismark Dakota . . . in the spring. Tellif and Ellen will come home with me if I can talk it in to him. . . I have thought some of going into the mines to work I can* [earn] *three dollars and half a day but I do not like to go down in the ground so far. . . i will stop i think i have done quite well and I will look for an answer soon. do not be afraid to me Carrie.* [sic]

from your cousin

Oscar Haines

****

A comparison of this letter with the following has convinced me that the date on the first letter should be January 15, 1887, not 1886 — Oscar hadn't caught up with the new year yet. We hear that Oscar has received a letter from Carrie, but her letters are lost to time. Carrie's comings and goings, feelings and fears are discerned only through Oscar's responses.

We wouldn't have these letters without the efforts of several generations of vigilant caretakers of these windows into the 1887 world, my grandmother Carrie, her eldest daughter Amy, Amy's son Robert and his wife Daisy Ann, and today their daughters Barbara and Kathy. These letters allow the voice of my grandfather Oscar to be heard, along with whispers from my grandmother Carrie. The close family ties are exposed, life in

Deadwood opens to us — all this as we continue to eavesdrop
on one side of a love affair.

Deadwood Jan 16th 1887

Dear Carrie

*I received your kind letter and was very much
pleased to hear from you and also to hear that
you are having a good time. you said that I
must not laugh at your letter there is no
danger of that as it is to nice to hear from you.*

*I should think you would not need anything to
eat all winter by the number of times you eat
[at] Christmas however you must have had a
good time. I'll bet there was good deal of
talking done ~~~~. I see that you have taken
in the skating rink if I am not mistaken you
said you was not going however I think it is
better for you to go ~~~~~~~.*

Those wavy lines at the end of the two sentences represent a
line drawn by Oscar, seeming to hint that he might want to say
more about that, or was a little jealous of those who were there
with Carrie.

*I am also glad that you have not cryed any you
must try not to get to tired as I want you to be
intirely well when I get back. You did not make
a success of mashing Albert Anderson. The
Father will do quite as well for the present.
You did not say how you and Mal was getting
along. I guess that is all right though.*

"Mashing Albert Anderson?" "The Father will do quite as
well?" And who is "Mal?" Mysterious talk, although Mal might

be Oscar's brother Melvin. Oscar continues — Carrie will understand and it really is none of our business.

That was a great letter I wrot to Aunte but I thought I might as well try I knew thay would have some fun over it and I would learn something by it. Thay must hae a great time out there with nothing to do. I hope I will be there next winter

Well it is time I write something about myself though there is not much to say one thing is certain I get plenty of work to do I have never worked any harder in my life though that is all right. I came here to make money and i want to make it if there is any to be made

i get the blues sometimes and i suppose if you were here you could help me get over them however they do not last long i have no reason for it. We worked all the holidays and do not have much rest on Sundays as there is allway some little jobs to be done that does pay to do other days

i came rather near getting hurt on Christmas day I was working on the road an a negro was out hunting Partrage with a rifel he shot at one toward me and the ball whistled by me within a very few fett and lodged in a bunch of shingles behind me. I thought it would have been kind of funney if i had been shot so soon after coming out here ~~~~~~~

I have not been down town yet since here and no where else so do not know anymore about the country that i did before. As it is past nine and i have to go to work by moonlight to morrow morning i had better go to bed. Lizzie says there is a lunch in the cupboard for me and i guess i will eat it as i am hungry as usual.

do not wait long before you write as i did not. I received your letter on Friday and this is Sunday night. It takes letters a long time to get here lately I have only[?] gotten one from mary and that was reproaches for not writing and I had written three weeks before.

well carrie I had better stop

from your Friend as usual.

Oscar Haines

The closeness of Oscar and his siblings is evident. They take care of each other. Oscar, Tellif, Lizzie and Ella living together, Lizzie caring for her brother Tellif's child, and leaving lunch for Oscar. Even Eli suggesting a visit to Sawmill Gulch with his "ponies" from Woonsocket, 360 miles away, and Oscar and his sister Mary exchanging letters.

But wait . . . there's more.

Chapter 43 — 1887 – Cousins in Love

Over a month passes before we get another glimpse of Oscar's life and love. Oscar and Tellif have moved from Sawmill Gulch to Deadwood:

I received your letter some time ago and should have answered it before but have not so and I have no excuse because I have had time enough but we have been moving around so much lately that I did not get at it. we have moved out of the shanty. Tellif has gone to the Hot Springs to see if he cannot get over the Rheumatism. Lizzie has gone to Galena to visit with a Lady and I am here alone so I have a picnic. I have nothing to do but walk around town, go to theater once in a while. I have tried to strike a job but cannot do so it has not suit me very well as my [ ] is about $8.00 a day. I [am] trying to sell the team if succeed I will probly strike for home if I do not get another job which is not very likely and I have not a very long time to stay anyhow so cannot take a very long job.

I want to take in Port Washington and Manitowoc on my way back so I must start a week early I do not know if Tellif will go back

with me or not. you said you was tired when
you wrote I could see that from your letter and
you had the blues to just a little. you try to do
too much I hope you do not get so tired often .

Two days later Oscar writes again, after he'd received a new letter from Carrie. Whatever Carrie wrote — Oscar was energized:

Wentworth Hotel. Deadwood, Dak February
24, 1887

Dear Carrie

I received your second letter last evening. I
wrote to you a few days ago but will write
again. I [have] nothing else to unless I go
downtown and Gamble. I spent two dollars
yesterday Gambling so I guess I will quit the
business. I think I will try to get a job as waiter
in this hotel. do not know if I can get or not
yet. I think I would make a good looking little
waiter.

You said you thought I wrote to someone else
when I get lonesome but you are mistaken. I
do not write to anyone when I get lonesome
because if I did you would get more letters
than you would want. I am Glad that Melvin
is good to you since one ought to be good to
you. you are always good to others when you
have a chance especially to me and I have
done nothing to deserve it or return [?] it.

You want to be careful and not work to hard.
I want you to be well and strong when I get
back. I would have given a great deal to have
talked with you a great many times this winter

*but as I cannot I will have to get along
without. I will have a great time when I get
back but we cannot sit up until twelve o clock
and talk as Melvin may get on his ear.* [No —
I don't know what that means. Author]

Then Oscar adds an upside
down and written up the side
coda:

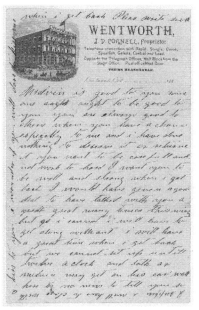

*well there is no news to tell
you so I will have to close
with a kiss to you. I wonder
if you will dare to kiss me
when I get back Please write
soon.*

The following letter talks
not of kisses.

It sounds quite formal
compared to the previous
message. Did Carrie object to
his familiarity? Or was it simply Oscar's mood from being sick?

*Wentworth Hotel. Deadwood, Dak March 11, 1887
    Dear Carrie,*

> *Received your kind letter yesterday and will
> try to answer it today. I am not feeling well
> today. I took a cold three weeks ago and does
> not want to leave me. Thought I would get
> started for Home next Sunday but the Doctor
> told me I had better stay a few days longer till
> I get better. I am Glad I am soon going Home
> and I am sick of laying around here. I sold our
> team yesterday and also Tellifs Lots in*

Spearfish but had to sell cheap as there is no money in the country. we are having summer weather the snow is almost all gone I bought some mining stock yesterday do not know if I will make anything on it or not. Tellif is getting better slowly he will come home with me. We'll try and get started next week some time You must not work so hard. I want to see you all well when I get home. I have not Gambled only a quarter since I wrote last. Excuse my short letter my head does not feel good. I would not have written till I was well again but said to write quick. I soon see you and tell you all the new.

Oscar Haines

"I have not gambled. . ." says Oscar. Perhaps Carrie did not look kindly on gamblers or dares of kisses. But the closeness and caring of this family is evident again in these letters, as Oscar sells Tellif's property while he recovers from the rheumatism, and talks of visiting Port Washington and Manitowoc, where his Aunt Kirsten and Uncle Elias live.

Oscar often cautions Carrie to not work too hard, not get too tired — Was she ill? A few hints in the letters suggest that Carrie was caring for Melvin's children, possibly live-in help. Was Oscar concerned that his widowed brother might lure Carrie into wifehood?

Two weeks later, Oscar, Tellif and Ella were home again, the local press reporting they had closed out their "general lumber business" in Deadwood. (*IND*, 1887-03-25)

How did it go with Carrie? Did they talk all night once again? Did Melvin have reason to "get on his ear" once again? Did they kiss? Or did Oscar have to start over with the courting?

Chapter 44 — 1888 – Tallak's Daughters

Lizzie didn't return from Deadwood with her brothers and niece:

> *Miss Lizzie Haines who accompanied her brothers Tellif and Oscar to Dakota territory last year, has concluded to remain there, having established herself in the business of dress-making. She is located at Galena, a town near Deadwood, and is said to be well pleased with her new home and surroundings.* (*DCA*, 1887-04-16)

Oscar's letters had hinted of Lizzie's independence, describing her "visit with a lady" in Galena and earlier her talk of going to "Bismark, Dakota . . . in the spring." I assume Ella came home with her father Tellif.

****

The town of Galena sprouted in 1876 when the first lead mines were successful in the area. By 1877 it had four hundred residents, a sawmill, three butchers, a livery yard, boarding house and post office. By 1882 it had added two hotels, more saloons, several stores, a physician, an assayer, notary, and a one room schoolhouse that still stands today. But Galena, located in a deep gulch surrounded by high mountains covered with timber, was devastated by the flood of 1883. Roiling water rampaged through the gulch, destroying much of the town, and ending the boom of Galena for some years. But it rose anew in 1886 as mining companies once again flourished around it.

That's when Lizzie got there. There were many opportunities for young, adventurous and good-looking women in the mining country, and despite the stereotypes of that city, not all Deadwood women worked in saloons or brothels. Many respectable women and a lively social set thrived in Deadwood and in the smaller towns around it. High society women needed quality clothes, and dance hall girls needed their own style of costumes — Lizzie might find a varied and fascinating clientele.

Tallak and the family knew that Lizzie was the adventurous type and had little concern when Oscar and Tellif returned without her. Tallak had other daughter problems at home to deal with, as reported in The *Advocate* just before Tellif and Oscar returned:

> *On the petition of Tallak Haines, of Nasewaupee, Miss Lottie Simpson, his step- daughter, underwent a judicial examination before judge McNally on Saturday to inquire into her sanity. The examination was conducted by Drs. Sibree and Mullen, who declared the young lady to be mentally deranged and she will be taken to the Northern Hospital to-day* [Wednesday].

> *Miss Simpson, who is an interesting young lady of about nineteen years, was a resident of Manitowoc where she attended the high school until last December when her reason became dethroned and she was taken to the home of her mother in Nasawaupee. Her trouble is said to have resulted from excessive study, and her friends hoped that she would recover if taken from school, but her condition has become worse until it is necessary to put her under restraint to prevent her from inflicting injury upon herself or her friends. (DCA, 1887-03-10)*

Sheriff Scott, who conveyed Lottie to the insane asylum, reported that Lottie was "very demonstrative while crossing the ice to Menominee, but gave her keeper no trouble otherwise." (*DCA,* 1887-03-17) The fifteen-mile sleigh ride across Green Bay brought the Sheriff and his charge to Menominee, Michigan, then stagecoach one hundred three miles to Oshkosh, Wisconsin, where Lottie was safely deposited in the Northern Hospital for the Insane. (*IND*, 1887-03-17)

Only a male of legal age could petition for such an examination, so we don't know if Lottie's mother Marie asked Tallak to take this action or if it was solely Tallak's idea. In the late 1800s, spending time in an insane asylum was not so unusual, particularly for a woman. Between 1850 and 1900, a husband, father or brother could petition that a woman be placed in a mental institution for behaving in ways the male society did not agree with. A male judge approved or disapproved the petition, a male asylum superintendent determined the treatment.

The uptick of feminine unrest as the voices of the suffragists became louder increased those petitions for commitment. The diagnosis of hysteria was frequent — indicating anything from sexual deprivation (or avoidance?) to an overactive sexual appetite.

Perhaps Lottie was just a loudmouth. Perhaps she had acted inappropriately outside of marriage. Perhaps she was truly troubled.

Four months after Lottie was committed Mrs. Tallak Haines went to Oshkosh to bring her daughter home: "the young lady has quite recovered her reason and her mental faculties are said to be as sound as ever." (*DCA*, 1887-07-03)

****

The Northern Hospital (asylum) in Oshkosh was a Kirkbridge State Hospital, designed by Dr. Thomas Story Kirkbridge who believed in "creating a humane and compassionate environment for his patients" which included a hospital with open space, light and fresh air for the patients. The treatments within those walls, however, were 19th century treatments, sometimes harmless, sometimes barbaric. A commitment for hysteria, for instance, often called for removing a woman's ovaries. We know nothing of Lottie's treatment during her four-month stay.

****

Around the time of the Lottie incidents, the Haines name got a little polish when Melvin Haines was elected secretary of the Bayview Lutheran Church. His brother Oscar joined the church and about that time the young men of Hainesville each donated $10.00 to purchase the first organ, with Carrie Rogn as the first organist. Carrie also received an offering in May. Carrie remembers those days:

> *We had real pews in our church and somehow we bought a new organ. I had the pleasure of playing the first times on that. . .*

> *Some of those who helped with the singing were Oscar Haines, Mary Haines, Kate and Con Jensen, Chris Rogen, Amund Olsen, Laura Simpson, and Gunder Bergsland.* (Carrie, *Church*)

There is Oscar in the same choir with his step-sister, Laura Simpson. Laura, age eighteen, was no longer living in Manitowoc. It appears that Marie Simpson Haines's three daughters had remained there until they had completed their schooling and that Laura and her sister Lottie, now back from the Asylum, were living with Marie and Tallak in Nasewaupee Township.

Tellif and Oscar were back in business, preparing for spring planting and getting their own names in the paper for the community to appreciate:

> *The first sulky plow ever brought into this county, so far as is known, was purchased for the Haines brothers, of Nasewaupee, through the agricultural implement establishment of Haney brothers.* (*DCA*, 1887-04-30)

The sulky plow was named after the racing sulky and looked like it. A few curved blades below the seat turned the soil, and voila! the first plow that allowed the farmer to sit while the horses pulled both plow and farmer. Some early reviews labeled it wasteful of horse power, but the prairie-sized acreage in the states farther west changed minds quickly, and the *Advocate* assured: "others will doubtless follow until every well-tilled farm in the county has one or more of these labor-saving implements." *(DCA, 1887-04-30)*

By July Tellif and Oscar were hard at it, and added the "patent loader" to their arsenal. They were leading edge on this one, which was considered too expensive for wide use until it became available through Sears & Roebuck in 1900, almost thirteen years in the future.

The *Advocate* reported that Tellif and Oscar harvested seventy-five tons of timothy in sixteen days using this patent loader "purchased from Haney Brothers." It went on to emphasize the savings in time and labor provided by this wonderful machine, then praised the Haines brothers for their exemplary management and investments in their business.

> *There are now one hundred and forty acres under cultivation, and as the boys own upward of four hundred acres in this tract they will soon have one of the largest farms in the county. The land was originally covered with dense growth of cedar and hemlock, nearly all of which was destroyed by the forest fires of 1871. (DCA, 1887-07-30)*

Some of that lavish praise appears to be the contribution of the Haney Brothers publicity department — these advertising tricks were all the rage — newspaper publishers and entrepreneurs buddying up to subtly influence the reading public.

Winter ended the farming and harvesting piece of the business, but Oscar, a pro at Green Bay ice crossings, tried another venture:

The ice on Green Bay is now considered safe for steady travel . . . Oscar Haines and Theodore Jacobson of Bay View have established a regular line which is making triweekly trips. They have a covered sleigh in which they have a small cast-iron stove which keeps the passengers comfortable . . . The ice is not near as thick as at this time last year but is considered perfectly safe. (IND, 1888-01-20)

One day later, the Haines Brothers tried that same safe ice to continue the distribution component of their business.

On Tuesday morning three teams left here [Sturgeon Bay] *and Idlewild for Menominee. They were loaded with hay, oats, flour and feed, the two first being owned by the Haines brothers . . . They all had a terrible time trying to get across, and the Messrs. Haines were finally compelled to leave a portion of the freight on the ice. It was bitter cold and this taken in connection with the fact that there was considerable water on the ice under the deep snow rendered it one of the most arduous and exhaustive trips that can well be undertaken. (DCA, 1888-01-21)*

January of 1888 holds the record for the all-time coldest temperatures in the upper Midwest. Green Bay registered 36 degrees below zero on January 21. It was the year of the "The Great Blizzard of 1888," which paralyzed the northeastern United States, but the Midwest had their share of winter.

By February the Haines Brothers are back on the ice:

[They] *have opened a flour and feed store at Menominee, at which the products of the roller mill in this village* [Sturgeon Bay] *are handled. (DCA, 1888-02-11)*

****

I would call this a reopening, since that news of a Menominee warehouse was announced when the enterprise was first formed in 1883. The article mentions the roller mill, a new competitor for the age-old grist mill. It replaced the stones of the grist mill with rollers of steel or porcelain, beginning the process of grinding finer and finer grains. As the roller mill improved, it successfully removed all the bran and germ, creating superfine white flour — remember Wonder Bread? (In the 1940s, the U.S. FDA required American mills to add back thiamin, niacin, riboflavin and iron to their pure white flour.)

****

One week after the opening of the new store in Menominee, Oscar writes a harried letter to Carrie across the waters to Sturgeon Bay, declaring his love, making it clear to us that the last few months had allowed time for courting, despite Oscar's ambitious business ventures.

> *Dearest Carrie,* he begins.
> *I have been lonesome ever since I saw you.*

Chapter 45 — 1888 – The Wedding

February, 1888

The letterhead for the Menominee store looks professional. But Oscar's writing is unruly and hurried — no punctuation and the worst ever spelling — transcribing accurately is uncertain. "I came over here yesterday and thought I should write last night but the House was full so could not." Oscar's thoughts tumble to the page, now barely legible, but I glean that he is worried that he missed church on Sunday and didn't get to see Carrie on Sunday night either. The letter is written on Monday; Oscar is wasting no time:

> . . . *Aunty told me that she thought you would feel hurt because I did not go out there but Carrie you did not want me out there more than I wanted to go. I do not want to hurt you hon you know that I think to much of you but somehow I am always doing [____] so Carrie I ask you for my sake and yours not to take anything I do so hard that it should hurt you but always be shure to tel me of it so that in time I may learn to do better . . . .*
>
> *sometime Carrie it seems if I should* [lose] *you I had lost all. you do not know how nice it is . . . to come Home and see you. I must close . . . so good by. whatever may come remember*

that I Love you and I know you Love me my
own Carrie . . . from your Lover Oscar Haines

There are no more letters, for us at least. Carrie forgave him. How could she not with the love expressed in that letter?

Oscar was back home in a week. Pastor Gjevre's availability settled the date and Carrie got busy with preparations. Invitations went out, were they written or just word of mouth among family and neighbors?

Then Carrie and her mother Helene huddled over patterns for her wedding dress. Helene, probably a little teary with the thought of her only daughter getting married, welcomed the chance to spend time with her daughter creating the dress.

Carrie's wedding photo shows the result of their efforts. The dress had obvious

Scandinavian touches, delicate lace trimming at the high neck and on the cuffs and the elaborate flower and leaf design on the lace apron that covered the front of the dress. But this dress was styled to the times, tight bodice to a little below the waist, offset buttons on the right and lace trim on the left, vertical tiny pleats marking the center of the bodice. The skirt was moderately full. The color of the apron appears white in the sepia photograph, the dress a darker color, perhaps a light blue — or violet or red or green — only the photo to go on.

This was a labor of love, taking many hours to design and sew, the magical sewing machine making short work of the long seams, but pleats and buttons, delicate lace, the flower and leaf design were all done by hand. The result was both figure flattering, elegant and yet reminiscent of Carrie and Helene's Norwegian heritage.

Carrie and her mother, perhaps her future sisters-in-law, Mary and Christine, all designed and braided rugs, sewed towels and bed linens, fashioned and sewed undergarments, stockings, dresses and shawls for her trousseau. Dress patterns were available but ready-made clothing for women was not yet in the stores. For Carrie, raised in the era of hand stitching every item of clothing, the sewing machine was more than she had ever hoped for.

Oscar was not idle in these pre-wedding months. He continued managing the Menominee store while preparing for the Haines Brothers spring and summer hay pressing season. But winter still had its sting:

> *Last Saturday night's snowstorm and gale was a bad thing for the roads in this town. . . Some of the worst places were on the route between Hainesville and Mr. Schintgen's farm. On Monday morning Oscar Haines started for town in a cutter, and although he had a hard time of it he managed to break through the drifts, but Jacob and John Senft, who followed with horse and ox teams, were unable to proceed and had to return home. (IND, 1888-03-16)*

Tellif remained in the Dakota Territory, spending much of his time in the new resort of Hot Springs. (*IND*, 1888-03-16) The resort, eighty-six miles south of Deadwood, had opened to the public a year before. Tellif was plagued with rheumatism, and hoped to find relief in the warm mineral water springs. It's understandable when snowstorms were still plaguing Door County.

Despite the transportation problems of a stormy spring and the excitement of his pending marriage, Oscar had found the time to join his father Tallak and sister Mary in the organization of a society to perpetuate the study of the Norwegian language and to create a library of books printed in that tongue. The Rev. Anders J. Gjevre, pastor of the Bayview Lutheran Church, had spearheaded the group. Carrie's father, Amund Rogn, another of the organizers, was chosen for the book purchasing committee, with the books to be housed in the home of Oscar and Tellif. "Our friends have done wisely in taking this measure to keep themselves familiar with the literature of their fatherland" quoth the newspaper. (*DCA*,1888-03-17)

And then the wedding day came. Oscar and Carrie were married on May 1, 1888:

It is rarely our pleasing duty to record a more suitable union than this . . the marriage of Oscar Haines and Miss Carrie Rogan . . . took place in Nasewaupee on Tuesday, the 1st instant. Mr. Haines is well-known to our citizens as one of the most upright and reliable gentlemen in this county, and one who through native ability and business talent has made his way to the front rank of our commercial magnates.

Miss Rogan is a daughter of Mr. and Mrs. Amon Rogan and is a young lady of superior attainments, winning manners, and a highly cultivated mind. It is rarely our pleasing duty to record a more suitable union than this, and it requires no gift of prophecy to assure us that a happy life is before our young friends. It is with no misgivings, therefore, that The Independent throws its handful of rice after the bridal party, and congratulates them upon their entrance into "the kingdom of heaven," which is only another name for blissful married life. (IND,1888-05-04)

A quick glance into the future via a 1938 *Advocate* article covering the 50th anniversary of this wedding adds a bit more detail:

> *The couple was married May 1888 by Rev. A. H. Gjlvre on the place where Geo Stockwell now lives. They settled on the old homestead which is now owned by John Jenson. Six friends were present who had attended the wedding fifty years ago. They were Mr. and Mrs. Theo. Thorsen, Mary Jensen, Amund Olson, Thorsten Larsen, and Isaac Skogen.* (DCA,1938-05-05)

I compared the plat maps of 1937 and 1877 to learn that the couple was married at the home of Oscar's sister Mary Haines Knudtson and then settled into the land owned by Oscar's brother, Eli Haines. This was the Big House built by Tallak — the house described fifteen years earlier as "one of the best dwellings in the county." (*DCA*, 1878-03-21) The house was located at the corner of the road to Idlewild and Hainesville road, leading to the cemetery.

Oscar was twenty-seven years old and Carrie twenty-one. Carrie's older brother Chris Rogn was one of the official witnesses, along with a neighbor. The wedding party was packed with family, those who were born in Norway and first and second-generation offspring. Carrie's parents, Helene and Amund, and her brothers Chris, Halvor and Elias were there. Tallak, father of the groom, at age seventy-six, was one of the eldest attendees and the earliest living Door County settler. Many of the neighbors attending the wedding had purchased their Hainesville property from Tallak or one of his children. Tallak's wife Maria would accompany him. Maria's children, Lottie and Laura, might also attend — Oscar and Carrie both knew Laura from church, and Lottie might tag along.

I wonder what Helene thought of this second wife of the man her sister had married back in Norway. Oh, she knew that he waited two years after her sister's death before he married Maria. But Oscar is Ellen's child . . . so Helene's thoughts might have gone.

****

My second son's first marriage happened in my home. An informal affair transformed into an afternoon of intrigue —my soon-to-be daughter-in-law had invited her father and her three mothers — her birth mother, the woman who raised her, and her father's new wife — and to top it off, the father of the groom, my former husband, was not speaking to me. I think Maria and her daughters may have caused some tension in the home of my Aunt Mary at that long-ago wedding.

****

I assume that all of Oscar's siblings attended: Christine and husband Hans, their two-year old son and Hans's two children; Melvin with Amelia, his fiancée, and Melvin's two boys, three and seven. Oscar's oldest sister Mary who had volunteered her home, of course would be there. But Oscar's brother and business partner Tellif arrived in Hainesville three days later, probably blaming slow transportation from Deadwood. Lizzie stayed in Deadwood. Eli and his wife and five children remained in Woonsocket, Dakota Territory.

All of Oscar's siblings were also Carrie's cousins. Tallak was Carrie's uncle just as Helene was Oscar's aunt. Were there any comments? Jokes? About this complex yet simplified family circle? What did Tallak think of this celebration? Never could he or Ellen have anticipated that their youngest son would marry the daughter of Ellen's youngest sister, Helene. That sister they had left behind in Norway forty-two years before.

The wedding was a simple affair in the home, a celebration for the neighborhood, and an intriguing event in the evolution of our family.

Chapter 46 — 1888 – Home Life

I interviewed my surviving Haines aunts and uncles in 1985, but only my Aunt Petra shared the subject of the first cousin relationship of Oscar and Carrie. She told me that the people in the Hainesville community were upset about the cousins Carrie and Oscar getting married. They didn't think it was right, she said. Petra, fifth child of Oscar and Carrie, was born ten years after the marriage took place and she had to grow up some before developing an interest in her parents pre-Petra life — I didn't ask her who she heard this from — wish I had. But there must have been some discussion of the relationship if Petra knew of it.

Discussion of the appropriateness of a cousin marriage wouldn't be surprising. By 1880 seven states prohibited first cousin marriages, starting with Kansas in 1858. Wisconsin's border state of Illinois passed its prohibition by 1890, but Wisconsin waited to enact its first incest law against cousins marrying until the early twentieth century. Between 1858 and 2005 thirty additional states passed similar statutes. Only Colorado has repealed its cousin restrictive law.

The United States is the only western country with laws restricting marriage between first cousins. Whether a marriage between first cousins harms their descendants continues to be debated today. Oscar and Carrie's 1888 wedding beat the Wisconsin timeline and escaped the felony charge, and by the time the law was passed all their children were born and Grandma Carrie was close to age 55. Happily, the law wasn't retroactive.

The newly married couple could simply walk across the street from Mary's house to the "old homestead" after their marriage celebration. Carrie knew this family house, the same place she and her family were welcomed when they first arrived in Sturgeon Bay from Norway, six years before.

Carrie unpacked her hope chest and took charge, arranging the linen shelves and dresser drawers to her liking. Her home and furnishings were much the same as the homes of her childhood, her chores much the same as those of her mother and grandmother. Up early to stoke the stove, trek to the barn to milk the cow(s), feed the livestock, gather eggs, then back to the house to pop the breakfast biscuits in the oven. Carry the water in from the pump, pour into cistern on cook stove for hot water, split the wood to fuel the stove. Oscar worried again about Carrie working too hard, now in their own honeymoon home.

Many ordinary farm families hired a young girl from the neighborhood to assist in the chores of the household, garden and farm. If Oscar didn't feel secure enough for this expenditure as his busy season began in May, he might consider it later in the summer. 1888 was a booming year for the Haines Brothers hay pressing, buying and selling services. Luckily:

> *Tellif Haines returned on Friday last from Hot Springs, Dakota, where he had been residing for several months. His health has improved during his absence and he will remain in this vicinity during the summer. Miss Lizzie Haines is now in Deadwood, to which city she returned upon her brother's departure from Hot Springs. (IND, 1888-05-11)*

So Lizzie stayed in Deadwood — still dressmaking? No further news of Lizzie until her return to Hainesville three months later.

But Oscar would be glad to see Tellif return. Despite the record low temperatures of the 1888 winter, spring bloomed early as the Haines Brothers began pressing hay in Clay Banks, then Sevastapol, both not far from Sturgeon Bay. By June 1 the brothers had shipped more than one hundred tons of hay and twelve hundred bushels of oats to Green Bay and Menominee.

They continued to purchase up-to-date farm equipment to expedite their work:

> *. . . The largest day's work in seeding ever done in this county was performed by Oscar Haines on Saturday last on his farm at Hainesville. In eleven hours he sowed seventeen acres of oats, the work being done with a spring-tooth seeder recently purchased from Haney Brothers, Sturgeon Bay. Ten acres in a day is the highest amount sown by other machines, and it has been believed that this record could not be beaten, but Mr. Haines has shown that the spring-tooth seeder can cover twice as much ground in the same time. (IND, 1888-06-01)*

The spring-tooth seeder was designed with the "sulky" seat for the farmer to ride his fields; now both plow and seeder allowed the farmer to ride instead of walking behind the equipment. The article goes on to report that the brothers plan to sow eighty bushels of oats, twenty-three bushels of barley, ten bushels of peas, several bushels of wheat, and one hundred bushels of potatoes. . .later in the spring. Very busy brothers.

The next month the Haines Brothers decided to close their flour and feed store in Menominee since they had a "a ready market for everything they have to sell right here." [Sturgeon Bay]. (DCA, 1888-06-09)

A new hay-press was their next purchase which they tested out on their father's farm, pressing twenty-five tons of Tallak's surplus hay. Tallak didn't play favorites though, and a month later hired a competitor to press another thirty-three hundred pounds (in an hour and twenty minutes with their nifty Champion hay press) — another of the news/advertisement blends. Perhaps Tallak made a dollar or two for the use of his name in the article-ad. His position as a pioneer settler and his natural business acumen might be valuable. (IND, 1888-08-31 and 09-21)

However, this could be Tallak's last harvest. Later that year, Tallak rented his farm to Magnus Larsen, intending to visit his son Eli in Woonsocket, Dakota Territory. (*IND*, 1888-11-02) His wife Marie isn't mentioned, of course, but she may have gone with him — or not. No further accounts of that trip, but before the next planting season begins, the *Door County Advocate* reports (and editorializes):

> *Magnus Larson has leased Tallak Haines' farm and he will carry it on for one year or more in connection with his own. Mr. Haines is upward of seventy-five years old, and the work of carrying on a big farm is too much for him.* (*DCA*, 1889-04-13)

Tallak was in fact seventy-seven years of age. And not done yet.

In September Oscar opened the Haines Brothers' warehouse in Sturgeon Bay, for storage of hay, oats and potatoes, probably to replace the Menominee store, closed three months before.

Oscar and Tellif and occasionally Melvin, transported their stored hay to the west shore of Green Bay after the ice was solid, using their own sleds and horses. This year they hired commercial schooners or steamships to deliver their product before the ice formed — the schooner *Elizabeth*, the propeller *Moore* and the steam barges *Noble* and *Sam Neff*— steam-barge referring to a propeller with a large hold for shipping. Sail and steam were still sharing the waters of Green Bay.

The Haines Brothers shipped 800 tons of hay and 2,000 bushels of potatoes by November 1888 and three or four machines were pressing hay "on their account." (*IND*, 1888-11-09 and 23)

It was a very good year.

Chapter 47 — 1888 – New Family Begins

Despite their busy schedule, Tellif and Oscar took some time off to enjoy another wedding celebration in July. The widower Melvin married Amelia Thorson. His two sons, three and seven, had lived with him during the two years since his first wife's death but his daughter Lizzie, now five, had been raised by her aunt in Baileys Harbor since her mother's death:

> *Mr. and Mrs. Melvin Haines went to Baileys Harbor Sunday to get their little daughter Lizzie, who has been staying with her aunt, Mrs. Stephan, for the last two years.* (*IND*, 1888-11-02)

The parting of Mrs. Stephan and little Lizzie might have been difficult for both aunt and niece, and Amelia had a challenging bit of mothering to perform. It was commonplace, however, for widowers to arrange childcare with female family members. And unfortunately, the death of young mothers from childbirth, overwork or disease, was not unusual.

Oscar and Tellif finished the hay pressing and produce gathering by October of 1888, and then Oscar and Carrie moved into Sturgeon Bay for the winter, "the business interests of Mr. Haines requiring his presence in town." (*IND*, 1888-10-05) Evidently Oscar would be managing the storage and shipment of the Haines Brothers merchandise. It was coincidentally about the time that Carrie was certain she was pregnant with her first child and she just might have informed Oscar. They moved into a "dwelling-house leased by Miss Anna M. Potter." (*IND*, 1888-10-05) Tellif would look after the farm, with Lizzie's help.

Carrie becomes a town wife. That sounds like a less demanding environment for Carrie, especially since they were boarding in the house with Miss Potter. A news article in mid-

December relates that Miss Potter had fallen because of a sudden spasm, and that Mrs. Oscar Haines, "who resides in the same building," heard the noise and summoned her husband to help carry Miss Potter to the couch. (She recovered.) It's possible that Carrie did not have the burden of usual household chores in this house and that Miss Potter's boarding house provided meals. Oscar evidently had retained his love-nurtured concern for his young wife and taken her away from chore-filled farm life for these few months before their first baby was born — even in this era when a wife's toil was often discounted, and childbirth considered a trifling matter.

Carrie and Oscar didn't spend much time in Sturgeon Bay. Three months after their move to town, they moved back to the farm in Hainesville on February 1, 1889, just in time. Three weeks later:

> *The household of Mr. and Mrs. Oscar Haines, of Hainesville was brightened Wednesday by the arrival of a little girl who is nice, like all the rest of her angelic sex. . .* (*IND*, 1889-02-22)

Pretty sappy announcement. But Esther Agatha Haines was christened a month later, with grandparents, aunts, uncles, cousins and neighbors gathering at home. (*IND*, 1889-03-02)

A happy beginning for their first little girl.

Chapter 48 — 1889 – Haineses and Hainesville

While Oscar and Carrie were getting to know their new baby, the rest of the family was buzzing on around them. Mary, Oscar's oldest sister was getting some attention from the media:

A lady in this vicinity is having a hennery built which she expects to have completed and in operation in about two weeks. The building is to be one hundred and fifty feet long, sixteen feet wide, sixteen feet high in front and ten in the rear, with a sloping roof. It is to be divided into ten departments, each to be 15x16 feet. Each department has a large door to admit sunshine and air. The lady expects to begin business with five hundred hens, and will work on a larger scale if she finds it profitable to do so.

Mrs. Knudson begins this week the purchase of hens and will stock her house as rapidly as possible. We hope that her enterprise will prove entirely successful. (IND, 1889-11-01)

Mary ended her widowed status one month later when she married John Peterson. Rev. S. Groenfeldt, minister of the Protestant Episcopal Moravian Church, officiated at the wedding. Evidently Mary was not bound to the Lutheran Church of her ancestors. (*IND*, 1889-12-06)

Nor was her sister, Lizzie, the baby of the family, and the last of the Haineses to marry. Lizzie was twenty-eight, and had quite possibly sown a few acres of wild oats. Her marriage to Thomas Gillespie, again with Rev. Groenfeldt officiating, (*DCA*, 1891-08-08) came after her two year stay in the Dakota Territory and several years of cultivating the social scene of Sturgeon Bay. She had started early; in 1885 she and twenty-one of her closest friends piled into two sleighs in Sturgeon Bay to surprise

Captain and Mrs. Stanley at the Sherwood Lighthouse. The Captain and Mrs. were prepared, however, and entertained their guests until three a.m.

> *It was so dark during the return trip that the driver of the leading sleigh missed the track, . . . got into deep snow and one of the runners broke through the crust, capsizing the vehicle and burying the entire party under the box. The overturn was so sudden that the girls didn't have time to scream. The occupants of the following sleigh came to the assistance of the shipwrecked party, whom they extricated from their imprisonment under the box, finding that they were more frightened than hurt. They arrived safely in Sturgeon Bay by 4:00am. (DCA, 1885-03-19)*

Late hours seemed to be regular party behavior and "surprise" parties, with no one being surprised, was another theme. The parties were spontaneous, yet well-prepared for. Well-stocked pantries and adept hostesses is certain, but how did the word get around so fast? In October of that year about thirty friends, including Lizzie and Tellif, gathered for a birthday surprise, and "as a matter of course the visitors had brought with them the fiddle and the bow, with an abundance of rosin." The dancing went on until a late hour "except . . . when the party temporarily turned to other diversions." Yes? (*DCA*, 1885-10-29)

When Lizzie returned from the Dakotas, Tellif would often accompany her to the community parties, and on New Year's Eve 1889, *The Independent* reported a contingent of Haineses when Lizzie and Tellif and Mr. and Mrs. Melvin Haines assisted "in making the [New Year's Eve] masquerade ball a success." (*DCA*, 1890-01-03)

Tom Gillespie was also regularly spied at various parties and dances around Sturgeon Bay, and he too had traveled the United States "to see the elephant of experience." (*EXP*, 1883-12-21) Inevitable that these two eligible singles should meet. Tom, a second-generation Irishman, had been born and raised in Sevastopol, just north of Sturgeon Bay, but in 1890 he opened a retail furniture store in Sturgeon Bay, occupying two floors and basement, all connected by an elevator. (*DCA*, 1885-03-19)

A good match. Both adventurous, social, and, it turned out, enterprising and successful.

Oscar got back to work shortly, and he and Tellif continued as the darlings of the Nasawaupee farming scene, hailed for their farming capabilities:

> *Among Door County Farmers: The Haines brothers, of Nasewaupee came to the front again this fall with most excellent crops . . . The boys have got farming down pretty fine it would appear. (DCA, 1890-10-11)*

They introduced their new all-steel press that summer, weighing only 4,000 pounds, 2,000 less than their old one. (*IND*,1890-05-23) But like all good businessmen, the brothers were diversifying even as they continued their hay distribution business.

> *The Haines brothers are purchasing all the good cows that they can get this spring, for the purpose of supplying milk to Schintgen's cheese factory. The boys realize the value of the cow on the farm if her product is properly utilized. (DCA, 1889-05-11)*

The farming community of Hainesville and most of the Midwest were changing focus. Overzealous wheat production had worn out the soil. Chinch bugs, attacking the already declining crops, cinched it. The gospel of the cow was spreading — bring the cow in from the wild, improve pasture grass, allow the manure to nurture the land, milk the cow morning and night and shelter and feed her in winter.

But farmers fought being "chained to the cow" and were particularly leery of doing "women's work." Caring for the cow, milking and making butter and cheese had always been the work of the women on the farm. But slowly the men were converted — the sale of cheese was becoming far more profitable as the State of Wisconsin backed the cheese sellers with promotions throughout the U.S. and Europe.

The tower silo appeared next to the barn, this upright design deemed the best after experiments with dugouts and square structures inside and outside the barn. Feeding the cows through the winter wasn't possible until the idea of fermented corn was accepted. The silos kept rising. Soon all of Hainesville was converted.

Hainesville was a village of Haines's. Its namesake Tallak and his wife Marie lived within its fuzzy bounds, and all Tallak's children were scattered around him. Oscar and Carrie claimed the "Big House," standing in the SW quarter of the SW quarter of Section 27, the house perhaps shared with Tellif and his daughter Ella and with Lizzie until she married Tom Gillespie. Oscar and Tellif owned the bulk of the land in Section 27, their eldest sister Mary and John Peterson lived and farmed across the road, Christine and her husband Hans just down the road, and Eli and his large family farming around some corner.

All your original land purchases, Tallak. Does that please you?

Chapter 49 — 1890 – Tallak

Well, Tallak, you are growing old. You were a young man of thirty-three when my story began, Ellen was twenty-eight. Now Ellen is gone, although she lived a better-than-average lifespan (in 1800) of sixty-three years. I was much older than you when we started the journey, but as you begin the final decade of the nineteenth century you have caught up with me. We are seventy-nine years old, Tallak, and despite the century separating us, I feel closer to you.

Your life expectancy at age seventy-nine in 1900 is a little over five years. My life expectancy in 2017 is nine and half years. I know how many years you will live. I have no idea how many years are left for me. But now you must age much faster than I — you must.

And I must get busy and finish this book.

How are you feeling at our august age, as we approach the age of eighty? Pretty good, right? You can take credit for creating the community of Hainesville. You have a young wife by your side. Your sons and daughters are all settled comfortably in Door County. Even Eli is finally back. For a while it looked like the family would be scattered around the country, what with five of your children traveling the west — Colorado, Dakota Territory — and then that reconnaissance trip that Tellif convinced Oscar and Lizzie to take, all the way to Tacoma, Washington. Well, I knew they would all come back, but you must have wondered.

You and Maria are celebrating your eighth wedding anniversary this year. Are you aware that most of your second-generation descendants knew nothing of your second marriage? And those who did had heard from their elders that it was a one-night stand? Even your probate records don't mention a second wife; your sons identify you solely as widower of Ellen. Was it you or your children who wished to erase Maria from your life? Your second marriage is a mystery. How did it happen? And how did it work? The hints are few. Only once is Maria acknowledged to be with you in your doings, and of course, named only "Mrs."

> *Nasewaupee Column: On Tuesday last Mr. and Mrs. Tallack Haines started from home in a rig intending to visit their son Melvin, who lives some distance from the old gentleman's place. Soon after starting the team took fright and becoming unmanageable ran away. When Mrs. Haines saw what was coming she managed to get out of the rig without difficulty, but Mr. Haines stayed in and tried to stop the horses. In this he was unsuccessful, and the wagon striking some obstruction he was thrown out. He was bruised quite badly and it was thought at one time that he would not live, but he is now rapidly recovering.*
>
> *No bones were broken, and he will probably be around all right in a short time. It was a narrow escape and an experience that is not to be desired again. (REP, 1891-06-18)*

"... intending to visit their son Melvin" implies that Maria is just one of the family. But the Mrs. is a bit spryer than you are — it was noble of you to stay with the wagon but it didn't end well. I am glad to see you proved the press wrong once again.

I wonder, Tallak, if you are as agog over the changes in your life, in your world, in the sheer length of your years, as I am today? Think of the changes in your life so far. You cut down trees before the two-man crosscut saw, farmed in the days of oxen, crossed the ocean when wind determined your speed and traveled the land on narrow forest trails. You heralded the changes from oxen-power to horse-power, and have already heard your son Melvin speak of the "horsepower" of his gas internal combustion boat motor. That horsepower will forever ease the life of the farmer, the logger, and the traveler.

You watched your town of Sturgeon Bay change from a village with three sawmills and nothing else, to the thriving thruway ship canal port linking Green Bay to Lake Michigan. Your town recently acquired the first toll bridge to connect the town of Sturgeon Bay with the village of Bay View. A swing bridge, I hear. The middle section pivots 180 degrees, takes twenty minutes to swing open, wait for the ship to pass through, and then pivot closed.

Have you tried it? Or are you loyal to the ferry? You owned property next door to the ferry crossing dock back in 1864. I am enjoying reading about the bridge-ferry rate wars going on as your new bridge gets established:

> The opposition of the ferry and bridge is getting hotter and more determined every day. The first of the week the bridge was charging foot passengers two and a half cents and fifteen cents for teams, and the ferry two cents for foot passengers and ten cents for teams. Then the bridge made a cut and charged ten cents for teams and foot passengers free. The ferry followed suit on foot passengers and reduced the fare for teams to five cents.

> [The ferryman] says he . . . will serve free lunch and beer next week. Undoubtedly the bridge company will do likewise. Gentlemen, keep the good fight up if you can stand it. The public surely will, and will appreciate your magnanimity. (*IND*, 1887-04-29)

Change is hard — but you all must have known that the bridge would win. Time is valuable — even when we die:

> The great advantage of the bridge was shown at the funeral of Mrs. Philip Dehos, which took place on Tuesday last. There were thirty-three carriages in the

*procession, and to ferry these across the bay would
have consumed at least two hours, as five or six trips
of the boat would have been necessary. Verily the
world moves, and this region is keeping well abreast
of the times.* (*DCA*, 1887-05-14)

I've seen changes in my life too. I won't bore you with them,
but I think you would enjoy exploring my century's world just
as you explored and mastered the world of your time. You and I
both saw the population of the United States leap forward: from
the date of your immigration in 1849 to 1890 the population
grew from around 23 million to 63 million. But, Tallak, that's
nothing compared to my lifetime. The US census in 1940 was
close to 142 million and by 2010 was topping 309 million. The
number of people on our earth is our greatest problem today.

I know you needed all those children to help with the chores,
but the reproduction habits of your time greatly increased our
starting point. We are much more prudent these days, at least
some of us. I, for instance had a mere two sons. True, they were
directly responsible for producing eight grandchildren. I lost one
at age two to leukemia. But you and Ellen suffered when your
firstborn died within days of her birth, and then seventeen-year-
old Halvor in the Civil War. And then later — so many
grandchildren. I'm sorry.

Chapter 50 — 1891 – Tourist Home

Your living sons and daughters are thriving, Tallak. Your sons learned the logging business, then switched to farming when the trees were gone — gone due to the logging skills of you and your sons, and to the final clearing done by the Peshtigo fire. Ellen trained your daughters to manage household and homestead and their own children as they appeared. Both your sons and daughters inherited your skills in bargaining, searching for tax deed deals, government bonanzas, swamp deed bargains — after you threw them into the property speculating business, selling parcels of land to each of them on the day they turned twenty-one.

But even your youngest son had to learn of the sorrow of losing a child. One more grandchild was buried in June of 1891. Esther Agatha Haines, firstborn daughter of Oscar and Carrie, died in the night of the croup. (*DCA*, 1891-06-20) She was buried in June of 1891. Carrie was eight months pregnant with her second child, Ethel Agnes Haines, who was born on July 7, 1891.

Esther Agatha was buried in the Hainesville cemetery, that beautiful spot on the hill close to the Big House where Carrie and Oscar were living. Family legend contends that Tallak's first wife Ellen was the first person buried in that cemetery in 1880. It was 1888, however, when the cemetery was formally named:

> *The new cemetery at Hainesville was dedicated on Wednesday of last week, the ceremonies being witnessed by a large number of persons. The Rev. H. J. Gjevre delivered in the Norwegian language an eloquent and appropriate discourse.* (*IND*, 1888-08-24)

****

One hundred twenty-five years later, my granddaughter Kaera was buried in the Hainesville cemetery, in the same plot as Tallak's granddaughter Esther. Kaera was two when she died of leukemia, a disease over which we have limited control today — like the croup in 1889. How could I not explore the lives of my forefathers and foremothers surrounding my precious granddaughter?

****

Four years after Esther Agatha's death, Tallak had to endure the death of one more of his own children. His daughter Christine was buried on the hill, the third of Tallak's children to die. Christine Haines Eliason died in June of 1895, just thirty-seven years old, after suffering from consumption for four years. She left her husband Hans and four children to struggle on without her. (*DCA*, 1895-06-08)

Your son Melvin, a widower raising three young children until his remarriage to Amelia, has been busy developing his Idlewild property. That land, Tallak, is a local goldmine. Melvin has enlarged your original home by adding fifteen "sleeping apartments" and a large dining room, calling it a "tourist home."

"The location is beautiful and the surroundings simply magnificent," stated the *Door County Democrat* in May of 1899. You and Ellen never considered the idea of a "resort." What kind of people had time to spend a week or so doing nothing, much less traveling by boat or rail to a place especially built to serve and entertain them? Did you see this description in the *Advocate*?

> *Quite a number of people landed from the Atlanta* [passenger boat] *Monday morning who were subsequently transferred to Mel. Haines' place near Sawyer harbor, where they will spend a week or so in rusticating.* (*DCA*, 1899-08-12)

Rusticating? Going to the country to experience life, to relax in nature? You and Ellen experienced the country every day of your life, and it wasn't a bit relaxing.

These city-slickers are crazy for the country. Melvin's Tourist Home is the first venture into the tourist business in Nasawaupee since Judge J.T. Wright built a small resort on the tip of the peninsula back in 1880. He called his resort "Idlewild." Door County history books claim that Idlewild Peninsula got its name from that resort. Is that true? What did Mr. Sawyer and Mrs. Sherwood call it when you first got there?

Mr. Wright's resort was a rustic place that began with camping sites, then added some cabins and a dining room. It advertised boating, fishing, camping and "romantic strolling and lounging." (*EXP*, 1880-06-25)

Nellie Grant, the daughter of General Grant, spent a week there with her friends and attendants in 1882 — big news. You must have known of it. The Knickerbocker Ice Company set up shop right next door and the ice-cutters stayed at the resort in winter. Mr. Wright's resort seemed to last just a few years. Nothing more was heard of Idlewild Resort by 1883, but the ice-cutting business continued. (*DCA*, 1882-07-27)

So Melvin wasn't the first to realize the tourist opportunity in Door County, but he picked the right time to introduce the venture again. The railroad had finally arrived in Sturgeon Bay.

The Ahnapee and Western Railway steamed into the town of Sturgeon Bay in 1894, crossing the bay on tracks laid on the existing toll bridge. Initially, the train had to pull out of Sturgeon Bay and Sawyer with the engine pushing from behind, at a speed of twenty miles per hour. A turntable was soon installed in Sawyer, speeding things up to the thirty to forty miles per hour average when weather was favorable and the tracks in good repair.

With the railroad transporting visitors from Chicago to Sturgeon Bay, the tourist business was on its way. Melvin's resort, a fifteen-minute boat ride from the railroad depot, was easier to reach than the resorts further north.

The *Door County Advocate* agreed that the train was good for resort business:

> *... with a little gentle booming* [advertising?] *— a little pain to make the attractiveness known — there is no reason why in a very short time it will not rival any of the Lake Michigan resorts. It may seem strange that a place of its size* [Sturgeon Bay] *situated as it is should never have had a railroad enter it. . . but now all that is to be changed . . .* [as] *the Ahnapee & Western railroad . . . has begun to run regular trains.* (*DCA*, 1894-09-15)

Were you in the camp opposing the railroad, Tallak? Your newspaper friends, along with other old-timers who had championed the ship canal twenty years earlier, held off the railroad competition for many years. But it's here. And it's big news for the Door County tourist industry. Melvin must have done a little "gentle booming":

> *It is expected by hotel men and others that the approaching summer season will bring more than the usual large number of tourists to Sturgeon Bay. Melvin Haines has already booked rooms for many parties at Tourists' Home and is confident of a good season in his line.* (*DCA*, 1901-05-25)

Melvin took care that his resort stayed attractive to the tourists. He created a bicycle route on the grounds, clearing out stones and filling the road in with dirt. The route was described as:

> *a delightful one, the riding good and the distance (nine miles) just right for a ride that won't tire. A dinner can be taken or, better still, bought at the end of the route, and after a few hours spent in rambling*

about the grounds the run back can be made with a zest . . . (DCA, 1896-05-30)

And then, he added Lucille:

One of the pleasantries for the visitors to the Tourists' Home is the trip to Sawyer harbor on the fine little gasoline launch Lucille . . .she can carry thirty-five or forty people. She has air-tight compartments, which makes her very buoyant, and to prevent her being "cranky" she is supplied with a heavy iron keel. She is . . .a model little craft. (ADV, 1899-08-12)

Who could resist?

****

Your children were hooked, Tallak. The resort fever spread, first from Melvin to Tellif and Mary, who eventually purchased the Tourist Home from Melvin and changed the resort name to "Idlewild Inn." Tellif remained the owner of the Idlewild Inn until his death, with Mary and Lizzie running it for him in his later years. (DCA, 1929-06-14) Lizzie was famous for her chicken dinners and Mary charmed the guests with her conversation and wit. (Carrie, *Aunt Mary*) Eli opened another resort on the Idlewild Peninsula called The Pines; his son continued the operation after his death.

Your youngest son Oscar went into the resort business on another piece of land that you had acquired in your early days in Door County. Sand Bay became the summer paradise of Oscar's sons and daughters, and of my own childhood and of my grandchildren today. Oscar's sons Ted and Lester continued the resort tradition in Sand Bay on land inherited from their father, and their children keep those resorts alive today.

Pioneers, entrepreneurs, explorers — your children, Tallak, follow in your footsteps. They prosper from their own initiative and resourcefulness, but they prosper also from the platform you provided them — your immigration to the United States, then your search for just the right location and your selection of the bountiful land of Door County. Then of course you bought a good bit of it, logged it, cleared it, sold the good parts to those children and to fellow Norwegians (and a few Germans and other paying customers), creating the neighborhood of Hainesville.

Chapter 51 — 1895 – Mailman

Enough about the children. Tallak began a new project himself in his eighth decade. It starts when his wife, Mrs. Haines, receives a visitor.

> *Mrs. Tallak Haines has gone to Chicago to meet a sister who is expected in from Norway and who will probably spend the ensuing winter in this town. (DCA, 1895-09-14)*

This sister becomes a prominent member of the community in short order. I defer to the chatty local news media to tell most of this story.

> *A post office will be established at Hainesville in the northern part of Nasewaupee as soon as the necessary arrangements can be completed. Mrs. Tena Torgerson will be the post mistress and the office is to be at the home of John Peterson. Mrs. Torgerson is a sister of Mrs. Tallack Haines and came here from Norway last fall. The office has not been named as yet. Neither has the contract for carrying the mail been let. The service is to be tri-weekly. An office is very much needed in that locality. (DCA, October 24, 1896)*

> *Miss Laura Simpson, who is spending her vacation at her mother's, Mrs. Tallak Haines, was in the city a couple of days this week assisting the post office people in settling up some matters. (DCA, December 5, 1896)*

Tallak's son-in-law John Peterson was the mail carrier, but after three months, in March of 1897, Tallak took over the job, "undoubtedly the oldest mail carrier in the county . . . being within a few months of eighty-five years." John wasn't happy with the small compensation — Tallak evidently didn't care. He was in good shape," able to walk ten miles at stretch a when it come to the pinch. . . despite of his good old age." (*DCA*, 1896-12-12, 1897-05-08, 1896-11-28)

Tallak kept up the route for two years, but then his good health abandoned him, and John Peterson had to take over — still not happy with the job. (*ADV*, 1899-03-11)

Tallak is once more described as a goner:

> *Tallak Haines, who has been lying near death's door for several weeks, is gradually recovering, but it is a question whether he will ever get about again owing to his advanced age. He was 86 years old last September. He lives at the home of his son Mel. (*ADV*, 1899-03-04)*

Luckily, by April:

> *Tallak Haines has recovered sufficiently from his late severe illness to resume carrying the mail between Sawyer and Hainesville. Mr. Haines is evidently a man that prefers to wear out to rusting out. He has been actively engaged in working and various business enterprises for more than seventy years, starting in when a lad of only fourteen. (*ADV*, 1899-04-15)*

Then the post office business in Hainesville faded:

> *Tallak Haines is having a good time since July 1st, when the contract for carrying the mail expired. If he lives until next September the old gentleman will celebrate the 87th anniversary of his birth. A pretty good age that for a man to possess with all his mental faculties unimpaired. (*ADV*, July 29, 1899)*

****

You did indeed make it to your eighty-seventh birthday, Tallak. News of your imminent demise back in March was highly overstated. It appears that you kept the mail coming from Sturgeon Bay to the Hainesville Post Office (the corner of John Peterson's parlor, perhaps?) for the three-year duration of this rural delivery. Your post office opened at the height of post offices in Door County communities, to assure that no one had to go far for their mail. But rural free delivery direct to the farm was becoming a priority in Wisconsin and would be the next step for Nasawaupee Township.

It was quite a conglomeration of family connections that established and ran that Hainesville post office. Maria's sister Tena appointed postmistress, your son-in-law John providing space for the office, your step-daughter Laura assisting in its establishment, and finally you, the family patriarch, the mail carrier? Definitely nepotism.

But what's going on with you and Maria? In May of 1898 the *Advocate* announced that she moved back to the home of John and Mary Peterson in Hainesville after living with her daughter Isabel in Sturgeon Bay for six months. But you were reported living with Melvin when you were sick, at the same time that Maria was living at John and Mary Peterson's home.

If the 1900 United States Census is correct, you are living a double life. You are first recorded on June 6 as living in Nasawaupee Township with John Peterson head of household, wife Mary, and Tallak Haines, father-in-law, married 46 years. A different census enumerator on June 18, 1900, believes you were living in Ward 4 of Sturgeon Bay, as head of household, age 86, married 38 years. Wife "Julia," age 63, and daughter Lottie, age 32, single. You are listed as owner of the home "free" — meaning no mortgage. In both entries, your age is incorrect, years of marriage is incorrect and how the name "Julia" got there, who knows?

However, between those entries the *Advocate* confirms that Maria has moved to Sturgeon Bay:

Mrs. Tallak Haines, who some time since purchased the Eli Nelson place, has removed here [Sturgeon Bay] from Hainesville and now occupies the premises and will remain indefinitely. (ADV, 1900-06-09)

In the 1905 Wisconsin State census your name appears just once, in the family of Oscar Haines, head of household, wife Carrie, six children, ages fourteen to nine months, and finally Tallak, at the end of the list, age ninety-two, father, but still married — all on a farm in Nasawaupee Township. Maria, age seventy-one, is again listed in the 4th ward of Sturgeon Bay but this time as head of household, married, and owner of the home free. As before, her daughter Lottie is living with her, occupation dressmaker. In December of 1905, Maria and Lottie are living in Los Angeles, CA, where her daughter Isabella and her family live. (*ADV*, 1905-12-30)

Why the separation? You could tell us, Tallak, but you left no hints. I will surmise. Despite a seemingly indestructible constitution, you might have become frail in your 90s, and although Maria was age seventy-one to your ninety-two, she might not be able to care for — let's say it Tallak — the old man. Or maybe she just wanted to turn the tables on the traditional role of women or maybe you had enough of wives. Your children were plenty, lived in your neighborhood, and evidently were willing to invite you to their homes.

****

The marriage didn't last "till death do you part," but it didn't qualify as a one-night stand. The roots of this marriage might have come through connections made long ago in Bamble, Norway, and spurred forward by the circumstances that left Maria a widow with young children. At the time that Tallak and

284

Maria were married in 1882, Maria had been struggling as single mother of her three daughters for eleven years. Maria's deceased husband Lars had grown up on one of the Høen farms in Bamble, Norway. Did Tallak and Ellen know Lars and his family in Bamble? He was eighteen years old when they left in 1846 and soon followed their lead, leaving Bamble just three years later in 1849. Maria, too, was born in Bamble, a mere child in 1846, but Tallak and Ellen may have known her family. Maria emigrated to America in 1855 and married Lars in Manitowoc, Wisconsin, that year. Tallak and Ellen might even have visited Lars and Maria in Manitowoc, especially since Ellen's brother Elias lived in that town too. Did Tallak learn about Maria's fate from her family still in Norway when he visited in 1882?

Or . . . Did Elias introduce a lonely widowed Tallak to Maria at just the right time for sparks to fly?

Whatever the connection, Tallak and Maria appeared to have lived together as man and wife for eighteen years, and Maria and her children became part of the community. Her daughters, Isabella and Laura, married Sturgeon Bay residents and began their families in that city. Laura had mingled with Tallak's children in the Bayview Lutheran Church and at the same social events as Lizzie and Tellif. Tallak and Maria struggled together with Maria's daughter Lottie, possibly a troubled woman, but nonetheless acknowledged as a local character.

No records of divorce action have surfaced, and both Tallak and Maria claimed the status of "married" in the census records. But they lived separately in the new century. There were no further mentions of Maria in Tallak's life.

****

Maria and her daughter Lottie continued to travel between Los Angeles and Sturgeon Bay for several years, then moved to Los Angeles. In January of 1920, *The Manitowoc Herald News* reported that Mrs. Lars Simpson Haines had died in Wittenberg,

Wisconsin and at her request would be buried in the family lot at Evergreen Cemetery in Manitowoc, next to her first husband, Capt. Simpson, or Lars Simonson Simpson Høen. Her gravestone reads Gunhild Marie SIMPSON Hoen/1833-1920.

Chapter 52 — 1907 – Tallak

Happy Twentieth Century, Tallak. After all those incorrect age numbers in the previous chapter, let's clarify. Your age at the turn of the century is eighty-seven — you will reach eighty-eight in September. I am still a sprightly seventy-nine. From the newspaper reports, however, your daily walks are several miles longer than mine.

But sorrow haunts your lengthy life with losses of those less hardy. In June of 1901, your sister-in-law Helene Rogan, Carrie's mother, died after an illness of one year. She was sixty-three years old; her obituary reports that she had lived in Hainesville for nineteen years. Remember, Tallak, when you went to Norway to see her, after you had been gone for thirty-five years? You pushed their decision to emigrate to America, even sold property to her husband Amund, sight unseen. And with Helene, you brought her daughter Carrie, destined to marry your son Oscar.

Helene's funeral service was at her home, but the *Advocate* reported that "forty-two teams followed the remains to the last resting place, it being one of the largest corteges ever seen in the town." She too rests in the Hainesville Cemetery on the hill. (*ADV*, 1901-06-08)

You are living with your children now, at least those in Hainesville. Sometimes Mary and her husband John, sometimes Melvin, but mostly with Carrie and Oscar. How did Carrie take her mother's death? It must be hard for her to process. Her grief is real, but her time is for her children now — five of them, the oldest age ten and her baby, named after you, by the way, Tallack Edward Haines, is five months old. They will call him Ted — sorry, but Tallack, however its spelled, is not a twentieth century name.

Carrie's father, Amund Rogn, lives close by, and he probably stops in to see his daughter and grandchildren, especially now after Helene's death. He's substantially younger than you, but you have much in common — your Bamble years, the journey to America, Helene, Hainesville, maybe fishing — Amund was a great fisherman. He spends some time with his son in Silverton, Oregon, but most days he is right down the road. Hope you had some good chats.

You are a lucky old man to have all your children living in Door County, most of them less than a mile away. I wonder if you ever wish one or the other of them was more distant?

My aunt Petra (your grandchild — she is the three-year old running around you in Carrie's house) told me that she and Ted were born at Sand Bay — the land that would one day become Oscar's tourist resort. There was no road yet. They skied or sledded in winter and rowed in summer from Eliason's place, not far. Oscar still owned the Big House and continued farming that land. The whole family moved back there after Ted was born, probably about the time you moved in with them. I'm sure you have visited Sand Bay to see what they have done there.

The *Advocate* checks in on your birthday in 1901:

> *Tallack Haines last month celebrated the 89th anniversary of his birth, and he feels as though he is good enough for another ten years or so.* (*ADV*, 1901-10-19)

But your losses continue to pile up.

> *John Peterson died Tuesday morning at his home in Hainesville of consumption. He had been ill for the past six months or more, but it is a question whether any of his friends believed that the end was so near. The deceased was a brother-in-law of the Haines brothers, and a man very highly thought of by his neighbors and friends. He was about 40 years old, and leaves a widow. The funeral took place Friday afternoon.* (*ADV*, February 1, 1902)

I'm sorry again, Tallak. You gain another year and lose a man who must have been a close friend as well as son-in-law. The widow, unnamed, is your daughter Mary, widowed for the second time. No children for Mary, but she lived a long, active life — took after you I think, Tallak.

I wonder, was it about now that you gathered the old trunks and looked through your lifetime of documents, trinkets? Was it about now that you gave the dearest to Oscar, your youngest son, perhaps some photos taken of you alone and you and Ellen? Was there a Bible, with those inner pages of births and deaths? Was it about now that you turned over the papers you received after Halvor's death, the heartless inventory of his effects, that proud list of all your family, the list you never showed anyone after you discovered that one of your family was gone?

The *Advocate* assures us that you are "still on deck" in August of 1902 and able to "get about" to visit your sons, occasionally on foot. The reporters were inspired to reflect on how many octogenarians were living in the town and vicinity. You were listed second oldest of the twenty-six counted, only five of them women. (*ADV*, 1903-01-10)

You are a hardy people, up there in the northlands. You must learn to treat your women better. We women outlive you men in my era.

Tellif, son number two, and his daughter Ella are reported to be in Pasadena, California, visiting "E.C. Daniels and family" and "will remain to gather fruit, flowers and swing in the hammocks." Coincidentally, Tellif is closing a deal to purchase a "considerable tract of wild land" that Mr. Daniels still owns in Door County. Like father, like son.

The newspapers continue reporting with great amazement of your activities at so grand an age. Driving a team to and from town, taking daily walks, visiting your children, your plan to walk into Sawyer (that's seven miles, sir) as soon as the roads are cleared, musing about whether you are the oldest man in the county. (*ADV*, multiple articles 1903, 1904,1905)

But I have another event on my mind. On Sunday, February 26, 1905, a baby was born in the house where you are staying. The newspaper notices this too: "Nasewaupee: A bright little baby girl gladdened the home of Oscar Haines on Sunday morning""

Tallak. She is my mother. Her name is Marion. Go see her, sit by her. Hold her. Your touch will reach me through my mother's hand thirty-three years later.

The newspapers begin a countdown:

> *Tallak Haines has been ill for some while back, and owing to his great age (93 years) it is only too evident that the end is not far off. (ADV, March 3, 1906)*

> *Tallak Haines is very low, and his death is momentarily expected. He is at the home of his eldest daughter, Mrs. John Peterson, who is assisted in the work of caring for him by her sister, Mrs. Thos. Gillespie, and other members of the family. Mr. Haines was 93 years old last September, being one of the oldest men in the county. (ADV, 1906-04-20)*

One week later, we hear that Oscar is "quite seriously ill with lung trouble." (*ADV*, 1906-04-13)

While Oscar is sick, Mary and Lizzie care for you at Mary's house. Good. Carrie has plenty to do dealing with her sick husband, two-year old Marion, Ted, five, Petra, eight, and the three older children, eleven, thirteen and sixteen. Carrie was in the classic clutch of the sandwich generation.

****

You recover, of course.

> *Talak Haines has recovered sufficiently from his late serious illness as to be able to get about once more. His son Oscar, who has also been quite sick for*

some weeks past, has nearly or quite recovered.
(*ADV*, May 25, 1906)

I don't believe this, Tallak. Again? One day those reports will have the last word, but you have certainly kaboozled them over and over again. And the spelling of your name continues to be haphazard.

Oscar recovers too, and you are back with Oscar and Carrie in the house you built in 1878, described at the time as "one of the best dwellings in the county" where "at no very distant day we expect to see that area [Nasawaupee] one of the most flourishing sections of the county." (*DCA,* 1878-03-21)

It's the distant day, Tallak. Remember the rock of your Høen farm? The disappointment in your land in Norway? Step into the doorway here. Look at this land. Think of your long life and your multitude of accomplishments. Think of your people, your children, your neighbors, your Hainesville. Your life, with the influence of the ancient cultures of the Native Americans, the many cultures you have mixed with, so many more than you would have experienced in Norway. You have shown your descendants how this uniting of cultures works. We simply need a little more patience, a touch more tolerance, and more stories like yours. Give thanks. Be pleased.

****

Oldest Man in County Dead

Tallak Haines, probably the oldest man in the county, died Monday evening at the home of his son Oscar, in Hainesville. Death was due to old age the deceased having completed the 94th year of his existence on September 28, 1906. He is survived by six children - four sons and two daughters - Tellif, Melvin, Elias and Oscar, and Mesdames John Peterson and Thos. Gillespie. Coming to Door county in 1856, Mr. Haines first located in what is now the northern part of Union. Remaining here until in the fall of 1863, he removed to Sturgeon Bay, and began making a farm of the land embraced in what is now a part of the John F. Nelson and Gergen Sorenson places. A year or two afterward he removed to the northern part of Nasewaupee, which has been his home and most of his family ever since. In the days of his prime Mr. Haines was one of the most active of men in both body and mind, and he was always regarded as honest and straightforward in all his dealings. The funeral took place from the home at Hainesville this afternoon, Pastor Masted officiating. (ADV, 1907-04-18)

Considering the bad roads and unfavorable weather there was a surprising large turnout at the funeral of the late Tallak Haines held from the home of his son Oscar in Hainesville last Thursday afternoon, between forty and fifty teams making up the procession. Pastor Masted preached a very able discourse on that occasion which made its impress on the hearers. (ADV, 1907-04-25)

Of course there was a "surprising large" turnout. I'm expecting a retraction any time.

The End

ACKNOWLEDGMENTS

I must start with Jack. He gave me time. He quietly cared for everything of the household, listened while I read, critiqued when asked, solved my technical issues and pushed me out the door to research adventures.

My grandmother started my history awareness with her brief but encompassing family history – without those three pages, covering 100 years, my search for day-to-day details would have been aimless. Thank you, Grandma Carrie, for your memories and for my early refuge at your farm of yesterday.

Thank you to my aunts and uncles, cousins and sisters, for your stories and for storing family letters, photos, news clippings, mementos of the family's past. The travels and genealogical records of my Aunt Alice and Uncle Ted and cousins Rachel, Adeline and Donald were invaluable, as was their sharing of family records. My cousin Bob, his wife Daisy Ann, and his children shared letters and photos. Amy and Karen nurtured and encouraged, providing a refuge at the end of the day. Thank you every one.

My sister Jeanne endured driving detours to research possibilities, peered through drawers of index cards, read faded newspapers, explored dark and soggy cemetery, and crawled through ruins of the Erie Canal. My sister Ruth listened and read through chapter after chapter, critiquing, encouraging, rejoicing as the chapters accumulated.

I am grateful for the history-aware community of Sturgeon Bay and Hainesville for access to records, objects, deeds, newspapers in its museums and libraries, especially the many missions of The Door County Historical Society.

Thank you to my fellow writers in the Rillito River Nonfiction Writing group. Collectively and individually you taught me to write. To University of Arizona Poetry Center –Lisa for expanding my vision and Fenton Johnson for opening the door to writing this book. To Meg Files at Pima Community College, her workshops and project class and for my fellow students in that class.

I am grateful for the services and hospitality of the Norwegian Genealogical Society and Naeseth Center in Madison, Wisconsin, the online sources of the Salt Lake City Family Center, Wisconsin Historical Press.

For my beta readers, Mark and Scott, Adele, Pat, Chuck, Ruth, Alex, Don, Jack and Adie, bless you.

NOTES

The names and dates of births, baptisms, confirmation, death are provided from
- Genealogy chart typed and formatted (pre-computer) by my cousin, Adie Haines from information gleaned from relatives visits with relatives in Norway – a joint effort of my Aunt Alice Haines and her son Don and daughter Adie and Rachel.
- Bamble Parish Records, The National Archives of Norway. Arkivverket Digitanarkive. Accessed at http://www.arkivverket.no.
- Bygdebok for Bamble, Vol II
- Naeseth, Gerhard B., Blaine Hedberg, ed. *Norwegian Immigrants to the United States. A Biographical Directory 1825-1850* Volume Two 1844-1846. Deborah, Iowa, Vesterheim Norwegian-American Museum. Anundsen Publishing Co, 1997.
- The Tanum Church Parish Records including those for Bayview Lutheran Church in Sturgeon Bay, Wisconsin made available via microfilm from the LDS Family History Center in Salt Lake City, Utah.
- **U.S. Census Records for multiple years accessed through Ancrestry.Com:** including Door County, Ozaukee County, Manitowoc County in Wisconsin; Port Huron, Michigan, Lawana, Dakota Territory and other areas as needed, and the Canadian Census for the Province of Ontario, Canada.

My grandmother's stories are cited in-text in short form:
- *Haines History:* ((Carrie, *History*)
- *The Story of My Life:* (Carrie, *My Life*)
- *The Happiest Day:* (Carrie, *Happiest*)
- *Aunt Mary:* (Carrie, *Aunt Mary*)

All by Marte Karine Rogn Haines, or, she says " better in

Hainesville" as Carrie Rogen Haines or Mrs. Oscar Haines.
Written 1944-45 and transcribed by Petra Haines Slotten.

Door County Newspaper Archive in-text in short form:

- *(DCA) Door County Advocate* 1862-1897
- *(DCA) Door County Advocate* 1918-1941
- *(DEM)Door County Democrat* 1893-1918
- *(ADV)The Advocate* 1897-1912
- *(DEM)The Democrat* 1892-1895
- *(DCN) The Door County News* 1914-1939
- *(EXP) The Expositor* 1873-1877
- *(EXP) The Expositor Independent* 1877-1880
- *(IND) The Independent* 1886-1890
- *(REP) The Republican* 1890-1892
- *(SBCA) The Sturgeon Bay Advocate* 1912-1918
- *(EXP) Weekly Expositor Independent* 1880-1886

Accessed at: http://www.doorcountynewspapers.org
Thank you to the Maihaugen Foundation, Door County Library
Foundation; their contributions made the database possible;
and to the County of Door, Door County Advocate, for their
cooperation in this project.

Individual Notes Section begins on following page.

Chapter 1—1845 – Decisions

Page #

5. "the law of Odelsret": Rasmus Björn Anderson, LL.D, *The First Chapter of Norwegian Immigration,* 304

5. "all on that 3% of arable land": Carol A. Culbertson and Jerry Paulson. *A Research Guide for Norwegian Genealogy*

5. "he worked on his own": Hjalmer Holand, "HAINESVILLE: An Old Seaman's Paradise."

5. one speciedaler equaled one American dollar: Ann Urness Gesme, Between Rocks and Hard Places. 136

Chapter 3 —1845 – Preparation

12. Never had so many made this bold decision.: Gerhard B. Naeseth, *Norwegian Immigrants United States.* 275-279

13. "three potter . . . of water for each passenger per day": Lovoll, Promise of America, 21

13. "the woman baked the flatbread. . .": Gesme, *Between Rocks and Hard Places.* 59

14. She realized four hundred speciedallers .: Betty A. Bergland and Lori Ann Lahlum, *Norwegian American Women,* 2011

Chapter 4 —1864 – The Leaving

22. to the port of Le Havre.: Sea Distances, 2015

23. "who specialize in taking care of immigrants. . .": Gosz, *Village Life,* blog.)

Chapter 5—1946 – All Aboard

25. "The cabin midsection held the family bunks, . . . enough space for five persons": Semmingsen, 58

26. about two and a half feet between the upper and lower bunk.: William P. Dillingham, *Reports of the Immigration Commission*, 296-303.

28. Halvor toddled around in a dress-like garment.: Gesme, 66

28. "spring lines were attached to the ship fore and aft . . .": Linka Preuss, 1829-1880 – *Linka's Diary.*

Chapter 6 —1846 – The North Atlantic

32. "a Halling tune, a fast, sharp folk dance.": Preuss, 22

34. "after weeks of salt herring and dried meat.": Preuss, 227, 234

Chapter 7 — 1846 – New York, New York

41. Passengers were along for the ride.: T.J. Stiles, *The First Tycoon.*

42. more like the open space they were promised.: Henn Wilson, *Illustrated Guide to Hudson River,* 9

42. "Lined with birches and cedars and dogwood.": Eric Kiviat. *Vegetation of Duchess.*

Chapter 8 — 1846 – The Erie Canal

45. "and so many choices": JoAnne Sadler, "Early Immigrants on the Erie Canal" from the *Norway-Heritage - Hands Across the Sea* website.

45. "cut through whatever or whomever it encountered in the coach.": Henry Priebe, Jr., "The City of Buffalo 1840-1850,"

47. "maybe a glass or two to ease the way.": Beulah Folkedahl, *Knud Knudsen and His America Book.*

48. "human bodies clustering all over them like a swarming hive…": JoAnne Sadler, "Early Immigrants on the Erie Canal"

Chapter 9 —1846 –Detour Canada

51. "sailing on the *Sultan* to New York City.": Naeseth, *Norwegian Immigrants to the United State,* Vol II, 275-279

53. boarding houses between Port Stanley and Sparta.: Hugh Joffre Sims, *History of Elgin County, Volume III,* 39

55. "Maid of the Mist ferry, launched in 1846.": J. B. Mansfeld, "An Interesting Description of the Lakes in 1847 by Thurlow Weed, Vol I Chapter 36.

56. "over twenty ships wrecked or run ashore.": Mansfeld

Chapter 10 —1848 – Wisconsin

58. "crowded with the passengers who boarded in Chicago or Buffalo.": University of Northern Iowa, "Helpful Hints for Steamboat Passengers."

59. "the view that revealed the true vastness of the West.":Mansfeld

59. "ten or more acres of land to produce that wood .": Mansfeld, 209

60. "log chute to carry the logs down from the bluff.": Kathy Noltze, *Ulao, Footsteps on the Bluff,* 21

60. a blur of green mixed with traces of the gold and red of early fall.: Price, *Hist of Port Washington*

60. seven families from a parish just south of Bamble.

Norwegian Immigrants to the United States.
Chapter 12 — 1849 –Port Ulio
68. "timber till all the trees around knew what was coming to them.": Richter, Conrad, *The Fields*, 8
69. a tradition the Norwegians had adopted from Germany in the 1820s.: Blixen, *Norway Christmas*
70. "and thought it good fun when they told about old things in Norway.": Wilson, *Life Among Settlers.*
Chapter 13 —1854 – The Siblings Scatter
73. "Elias married Andrea in 1853 in Valdres.": Wisconsin Historical Society
73. Cholera swept the settlement.": Histories Ozaukee County, 1881
75. "tons of saleratus and potash, fish, lumber and hides." Potash was created by boiling the ashes of burnt trees and, like today, used for fertilizer. But further purifying of potash, through many steps of boiling and fermenting, created saleratus, which was popular as a leavening agent for making bread and biscuits. Saleratus was edged out by baking soda in about 1860.: Mary Jane Frances Price, *The history of Port Washington, in Ozaukee County, Wisconsin*, 37
75. teach their predominantly German students in their common native language.: Price, 39
76. Norwegian friends had already left for places farther west or north.: Noltze, 41
Chapter 14 — 1855 – By Land and Wagon
77. That's all it took to create an ox.: Price, 37
78. government treaties continued to push the tribes further west.: Sam Perlman, "The First Door County Residents."
78. British and American military widened it to accommodate marching troops, : H.E. Cole, "The Old Military Road." 53.
78. all packed into a space about four feet wide by twelve feet long.: Randolph Marcy, *The Prairie Traveler.*
79. lift the ox off the ground for shoeing. Michael Williams, "The Living Tractor."
79. Their possessions were further protected from rain and dust [in a covered wagon]: Laura Ingalls Wilder, *Little House on Prairie,* 20.
80. Did Tallak have a military model Colt hidden in the jockey box? : "Pioneer Guns," *Tuolumne County Historical Society*

82. "city of mansions built by the British next to log cabins built by the old traders and the recent rush of immigrants.: History of Green Bay.

Chapter 15 — 1856 – By Land and Sea

83. the first European to discover Lake Michigan and the land that become the State of Wisconsin.: Jean Nicolet, *The Encyclopedia Britanicca*

85. Not even a general store had yet appeared in rough and tumble Sturgeon Bay.: Hjalmar Holand, *History of Door County,* Vol I

Chapter 16 — 1857 – Sugar Creek

89. various tribes still lived in the neighborhood.: Perlman.

90. "widow-maker," a felled tree caught in the branches of neighbor tree.: *The Wisconsin Logging Book, 12.*

91. cut through a mammoth log, sometimes three or four feet in diameter: "Saws."

94. Christmas in Norway.:Odd S. Lovell, "Norwegian American Cuisine"

Chapter 18 — 1860 – Trinket, Ponies and Schooling

101. It appears that Hjalmer had an exclusive — Tallak's adventures as told by Tallak,: Hjalmar.

102. The local Native Americans traditionally traded for colored . . . sometimes fish and game. : John W. Kincheloe III, "Earliest American Explorers" 47.

102. "Here was a good place for bartering,": Holand, *History of Door County,* 409.

104. "[we] children received but a meager amount of schooling.": *Commemorative Biographical Records of the Counties of Brown, Kewaunee & Door, Wisconsin.*

103. was likely the language spoken in the early schools of Union.: Holand, *History of Door County*, 142.

Chapter 19 — 1862 – Civil War

107. if that quota was not met a draft would be established.: David Ellison, "The Civil War Draft in Plover and Steven's Point"

108. They boarded a steamer on the Mississippi. Gene Estension, "Chapter 2, The Norwegian Regiment in Civil War"

109. I wonder if Halvor realized that he fought in a battle of major importance in this uncivil Civil War.: "Battle of Island No. Ten," Wikipedia

Chapter 20 — 1862 – Halvor

115. 241 men from disease.: Frederick Dyer, Compendium of War of the Rebellion

Chapter 22 — 1863 – Sturgeon Bay

121. "approved the name change to Sturgeon Bay.": Martin, Charles R. "Otumba" [Sturgeon Bay], *History of Door County, Wisconsin,* 27.

121. "Father Allouez": Hjalmar Holand, History of Sturgeon Bay, Door County, Wisconsin (Part I).

123. "by 1881 Nasawaupee Township included Yankees from New York, Connecticut, Massachusetts [etc.]: Martin, 26-25.

123. "Mr. Hanson had been a carpenter and ship builder in Norway.": Lynette Thonne, compiler. "Walk in the Footsteps." *The Hanson House and Family Story.*

124. The Historical Society has dug deeply into the family story of Hans,: Thonne.

124. "The Moravians . . . in 1864 dedicated the first church building in Sturgeon Bay.: Holand, *History of Sturgeon Bay*

124. yet thrived again in the 1700s.: *Moravian Church in North America.* "A Brief History of the Moravian Church."

124. and the scow was pulled across, hand-over-hand.: Holand, *History of Sturgeon Bay.*

125. The first school in Sturgeon Bay had a few pupils as early as 1856 *Peninsula Genealogical Society. Schools.* "Town of Sturgeon Bay."

Chapter 23 — 1864 – Idlewild Peninsula

128. Sawyer's Harbor, . . . was named after him.: Martin, 28-29

128. For years it was believed that he had buried his treasure somewhere on the peninsula, but it was never found.: Beth Robertson Young, *Old Idlewild,* 9.

130. There's even evidence that Tallak ran his logging camps from Idlewild.: Holand, "Hainesville: An Old Seaman's Paradise.

Chapter 24 — 1865 – Deeds and Deeds

138. no requirement for residence on or cultivation of the land

Homestead.: Homestead Congress. *U.S. Land Laws*. Friends of Homestead National Monument of America.

139. "The number of Norwegians emigrating jumped from four thousand in 1865 to fifteen thousand seven hundred in 1866.": Odd S. Lovell, "Norwegian Americans," accessed on 1-26-2017.

Chapter 25 — 1866 – Gentlewoman and Pioneer

142. Readers taught honesty, charity . . , and respect for parents.: The McGuffey Readers - 1836 version

Chapter 26 — 1867 – Suffrage Delayed

147. Elizabeth Cady Stanton and Lucretia Mott met in Seneca Falls, N.Y. to begin the work to achieve voting rights for women?: Women's Rights Timeline. Leonor Annenberg Institute for Civics.

147. President Andrew Johnson stalled reconstruction legislation,: Andrew Jackson. Conservapedia.

150. "quoted Bible teachings that women should be kept out of public life.": Women's Right to Vote in Norway.

Chapter 27 — 1871 – A Terrible Visitation

151. where he worked in the mines for four years.: Historical Society of Idaho Springs. "Historical Events and People."

151. He [Melvin] returned to Wisconsin in 1872.: Commemorative Biographical Records of the Counties of Brown, Kewaunee & Door, Wisconsin. Pg 631-632.

151. "strong and wild in both body and spirit,": Robert W. Wells, *Fire at Peshtigo*, 18.

Chapter 28 — 1871 –The Peshtigo Fire

161. "Expect up to 500, with more dead in Menakaunee and Sugar Bush": Charles I. Martin, History of Door County: The Great Fire.

162. "2 mills, . . . 148 dwelling houses and the same number of barns were destroyed.": Martin, 102-105.

162. destroyed over two thousand square miles of forest land, and killed two hundred people.: J.R. Manning, *The Worst Fire in America History*.

163. the weather conditions of the night were enough to explain the outbreak.: Christian Matthew Lyons, The Deadliest Forest Fire in American History: The Great Peshtigo Fire of 1871.

163. conservation of natural resources and regulations.: United States Dept. of the Interior. National Register of Historic Places Inventory - Nomination Form for Peshtigo Fire Cemetery.

163. they recreated those elements for the fire bombings of German and Japanese cities.: G. Tasker, *Worst fire largely unknown*.

Chapter 29 — 1872 – Recovery

165. "licked up and carried out of existence by the fire,": Martin, "The Great Fire." 102-105.

165. "first public school on the northwest corner of Fifth Avenue and Michigan Street in 1870." Ann Jenkins and Maggie Weir. *Images of America: Sturgeon Bay*, 78.

167. logging continued for many years to the north.: Martin, The Great Fire, 197.

168. "many were looking to America as a way to start anew.": Semmingsen, Norwegian Emigration to America in the 19th Century, 66.

Chapter 30 — 1872 – Carrie and her Family

172. "curious longing for the quiet of the solitary saeters and brisk mountain air"; Samuel Beckett, J. F.R.P.S., *The Fjords and Folk of Norway*, 68.

172. If Carrie and her brothers attended school, it would be the "folkeskol": History of Education in Norway. Norway, Norway Education.

Chapter 31 — 1875 – Growing Older

175. a traveling pastor who reached out into the more distant homesteads.: Holand, History of Sturgeon Bay, Door County, WI (Part 1).

175. Tellif was his partner in this venture.: Commemorative Biographical Records of the Counties of Brown, Kewaunee & Door, Wisconsin. 631-632.

177. Calamity Jane was living in town as Tallak and Tellif rode in.: 1876 Deadwood, S.D. *Wild Bill Hickok*.

178. "called The House for many years.": Holand, "Hainesville, An Old Seaman's Paradise."

Chapter 32 — 1880 – Ellen

184. one was a hospital for the insane.: Ronald L. Numbers and Judith Walzer Levitt, *Wisconsin Medicine: Historical Perspective*.

Chapter 33 — 1882 – Widower Tallak

189. Melvin received a letter from his father.: It was Carrie who wrote that "(Tallak and Ellen) didn't write." Melvin's disclosure to the newspaper suggests again that perhaps Tallak did not write in Norwegian, but was literate in English. Certainly Melvin would have no reason to learn to read in Norwegian.

Chapter 34 — 1882 – Bamble to America

193. increased number of migrants taking the train the 126 miles to Liverpool.: Nicholas J. Evans, *Hands across the Sea.* "Migration from Northern Europe to America via Port of Hull, 1848-1914."

193. single screw with one funnel and three masts.: *Passenger Ships and Images.*

194. Helene and Amund were at sea for approximately eight days.: NewYork, NewYork; MicrofilmSerial: M237,1820-1897. Roll451; Line: 1; List Number: 638.

195. swindled new arrivals on the open East River docks.: *The Immigration Process At Castle Garden.*

196. 6,949 immigrants passing through Castle Garden in the week that Helene and Amund arrived in New York City that week.: New York City Newspaper, 1882-05-?

197. arm and torch of the Statue of Liberty.: Megan Margino, Megan. *The Arm That Clutched the Torch: The Statue of Liberty's Campaign for a Pedestal.*

198. 26,966 Norwegians arriving in America in that year.: "Norwegian Americans," *Wikipedia, The Free Encyclopedia.*

Chapter 35 — 1882 – Immigrants Reunion

201. The water-powered sawmill was invented in the 1500s: *Water Wheel Sawmill.* Norwegian Genealogy and Then Some.

201. exporting boards to many European countries who lacked the wood needed for construction as early as 1700E.I. Couri and Jens E. Olesen, eds. *The Cambridge History of Scandinavia: Volume 2, 1590-1870.*

203. "the Staunch and Speedy Side-Wheel Steamboat Corona.": Door County Maritime Museum.

Chapter 36 — 1883 – Romance for the Old

208. Emigrating from Bamble, Norway in 1855.: Gerhard B. Naeseth, *Norwegian Immigrants United States.*

Chapter 37 — 1883 – Family Upheaval

213. last manned lighthouse on the Great Lakes.: Door County Maritime Museum website.

213. because of problems securing clear title to the land.": Door County Maritime Museum.

Chapter 38 — 1883 – Oscar and Lizzie on the Road

215. Tacoma would be their western terminus.: "Tacoma, Washington," *Wikipedia, The Free Encyclopedia.*

215. The population of Tacoma grew from 1,098 in 1880 to 36,006 in 1890.: David Wilma and Walt Crowley. "Tacoma — Thumbnail History."

216. "woolen underwear should be worn both summer and winter, and a shawl or extra wrap should always be at hand." Appleton's General Guide to the United States and Canada New Revised Edition.

217. "Until you have undertaken this journey": "California, for Health, Pleasure and Residence."

Chapter 39 — 1883 – Travels of Discontent

221. "broad streets that cross each other at right angles.": Appleton's Guide

221. The Chinese were our allies during WWII.: US Department of State: Office of the Historian.

Chapter 40 — 1884 – Church, Hay, Sorrow

227. Rev. Magelssen served the congregations of Sawyer, Manitowoc and Tanum,: Holand. *History of Door County, Wisconsin, The County Beautiful.*

227. Tallak's son Melvin joined the group at its second organizational meeting.: *75th Anniversary Bay View Evangelical Lutheran Church.* Booklet. 12-13

229. dropping a weight from the second story of the barn to press the hay.: "History of the Hay Press."

Chapter 41 —1886 – Death and Travel

234. only rusting mining equipment remaining. "Carbonate, South Dakota," Wikipedia.

Chapter 44 —1888 – Tallak's Daughters

245. it rose anew in 1886 as mining companies once again flourished Lawrence County.: Lawrence County - Crows Peak.pdf. Provenance unknown.

247. behaving in ways the male society did not agree with.: Jeffrey F. Geller, Women of the Asylum: Voices from Behind the Walls.

247. a hospital with open space, light and fresh air for the patients.: Pennsylvania Hospital Newsletter of the Friends of the Hospital in Historic Asylums of America.

247. often called for removing a woman's ovaries.: T.G. Morton, "Removal of the Ovaries as a Cure for Insanity," American Journal of Insanity 49 (1892): 397–401.

248. each donated $10.00 as an offering for Carrie Rogn, the church organist.: 75th Anniversary Booklet of the Bay View Evangelical Lutheran Church, Booklet p15.

249. until it became available through Sears & Roebuck. : Steven R. Hoffbeck, The Haymakers: A Chronicle of Five Farm Families.

250. "It was the year of the "The Great Blizzard of 1888,": Christopher C. Burt, "The Great Blizzard of 1888; America's Greatest Snow Disaster."

251. add back thiamin, niacin, riboflavin and iron to their pure white flour.: Theodore R. Hazen, "How the Roller Mills Changed the Milling Industry."

Chapter 45 — 1888 –The Wedding

257. Chris Rogn was one of the official witnesses, : LDS History Center: Tanum Lutheran Church Parish Records for Bayview Parish. Microfilm records, 82.

Chapter 46 — 1888 –Home Life

261. Only Colorado has repealed its cousin restrictive law.: Paul D.B. and Spencer H.G. "It's Ok, We're Not Cousins by Blood: The Cousin Marriage Controversy in Historical Perspective."

Chapter 48 — 1889 – Haineses and Hainesville

270. The silos kept rising. Soon all of Hainesville was converted.: Edward Janus, Creating Dairyland. Audio production Chris Bocast for Divergent Arts Ltd.

Chapter 51 — 1895 Mailman

283. to assure that no one had to go far for their mail.: James B. Hale, "The US Mail comes to Door County." October, 2013. Accessed at http://doorcounty.net/article-20364-door-county-history-the-us-mail-comes-to-door-county.html on 5-25-2017.

286. Her gravestone reads Gunhild Marie SIMPSON Hoen/1833-1920.: Find a Grave. https://www.findagrave.com/memorial/95207966/gunild-marie-hoen.

BIBLIOGRAPHY

"Battle of Island Number Ten." *Wikipedia, The Free Encyclopedia.* https://en.wikipedia.org/w/index.php?title=Battle_of_Island_N umber_Ten&oldid=673440313 and "Capture of New Orleans,"title=Capture_of_New_Orleans&oldid=683181879.

"Carbonate, South Dakota." Wikipedia, The Free Encyclopedia, https://en.wikipedia.org/w/index.php?title=Carbonate,_South_ Dakota&oldid=681628930 accessed April 23, 2016.

"Norwegian Americans," *Wikipedia, The Free Encyclopedia,* accessed at https://en.wikipedia.org/w/index.php?title=Norwegian_Americ ans&oldid=698145372 on January 11, 2016.

"Tacoma, Washington." *Wikipedia, The Free Encyclopedia,* https://en.wikipedia.org/w/index.php?title=Tacoma,_Washingt on&oldid=707331862 accessed March 4, 2016.

"California, for Health, Pleasure and Residence." as quoted by Appleton's Guide.

"Christmas Tree and its Origins - Christmas in Scandinavia," *Norway Christmas in History,* Copyright 2009-2012. Accessed at http://www.scandinavianchristmastraditions.com/christmastree. html.

"Helpful Hints for Steamboat Passengers": *Explorations in Iowa History Project.* University of Northern Iowa. Original at

State Historical Society of Iowa 2003. Accessed at
https://iowahist.uni.edu/Frontier_Life/Steamboat_Hints/Steamb
oat_Hints2.htm. (Cabins, Deck Passage)

"History of the Hay Press." Farm Collector. Copyright 2016,
Ogden Publications, Inc. Topeka, Kansas 66609-1265.

"Immigrants to Canada, Excerpts from the Immigration Report
of 1853." Accessed at
http://jubilation.uwaterloo.ca/marj/genealogy/reports/report185
3.html.

"Pioneer Guns" *Tuolumne County Historical Society,
Tuolumne County Museum and History Research Center*
Sonora, CA 95370-4920. Accessed at
http://www.tchistory.org/TCHISTORY/pioneer_guns.htm.

"Port Washington History," *Histories of Washington and
Ozaukee Counties*, Western Publishing, 1881. Accessed online
at roots.web an Ancestry.com community.

"Saws" *Colonial Williamsburg*. Accessed at
http://www.history.org/almanack/life/tools/tlsaw.cfm on
January 3, 2017.

"Water Wheel Sawmill." Norwegian Genealogy and Then
Some. Accessed at
http://martinroe.com/blog/index.php/2017/03/01/video-
wednesday-water-wheel-sawmill/ on March 4, 2017.

1876 Deadwood, S.D. *Wild Bill Hickok.* accessed on 2-3-17 at
https://www.deadwood.com/history/famouscitizens/wildbillhic
kok/.

75th Anniversary Bay View Evangelical Lutheran Church.
Booklet.

Anderson, Rasmus Björn, LL.D. *The First Chapter of Norwegian Immigration: Its Causes and Results 1821-1840.* Madison, WI. Author, 1906. https://archive.org/stream/firstchapternor00anderich#page/304/mode/2up.

Andrew Jackson. Conservapedia. The Trustworthy Encyclopedia. Accessed on 1-24-2017 at http://www.conservapedia.com/Andrew_Johnson.

Appleton's General Guide to the United States and Canada New Revised Edition. Appleton and Company, New York. 1881 HathiTrust Digital Library p. xiv.

Beckett, Samuel J. F.R.P.S. *The Fjords and Folk of Norway Methuen & Co, Ltd. London, 1915.*

Bergland, Betty A. and Lahlum, Lori Ann, ed. *Norwegian American Women, Migration, Communities, and Identities.* Minnesota Historical Society Press, 2011. www.mhspress.org.

Burt, Christopher C. *The Great Blizzard of 1888; America's Greatest Snow Disaster.* Accessed at WunderBlog News and Blogs on 3-15-2012. https://maps.wunderground.com/blog/weatherhistorian/comment.html?entrynum=65.

Cole, H.E. "The Old Military Road," *The Wisconsin Magazine of History.* Schafer, Joseph, Ed. September 1925 Vol IX, No.1, Ohio: Evangelical Publishing House Map.

Commemorative Biographical Records of the Counties of Brown, Kewaunee & Door, Wisconsin. J.H. Beers & Co. Chicago, Ill. 1895.

Couri, E.I. and Jens E. Olesen, eds. *The Cambridge History of Scandinavia: Volume 2, 1590-1870.*

Cambridge University Press 2016. Accessed at Google Books at https://books.google.com/books on March 3, 2017.

Culbertson, Carol A. and Jerry Paulson, *A Research Guide for Norwegian Genealogy*. Madison, The Norwegian American Genealogical Center and Naeseth Library, 2013.

Deed dated 8-19-1857. Recorded in Door County, WI 11-7-1857. Copy received by M.L. Forier from original record in the Door County Courthouse, Sturgeon Bay, WI.

Definitive Laura Ingalls Wilder & Little House on the Prairie: Little House Crafts & Activities. "Packing Your Covered Wagon" Accessed at http://www.laurasprairiehouse.com/crafts/packingyourcovered wagon.html.

Dillingham, William P. presenter, *Reports of the Immigration Commission. Abstract of Reports of the Immigration Commission*, Volume II. Washington Government Printing Office 1911.

Door County Maritime Museum website. Accessed at www.dcmm.org/cana-issland-lighthouse/door-county-lighthouses/sherwood-point, on 2-14-2016.

Door County Maritime Museum, Door County Maritime Museum & Lighthouse Preservation Society, Inc. Sturgeon Bay Museum 120 N. Madison Ave., Sturgeon Bay, WI 54235.

Dyer, Frederick H. "A Compendium of the War of the Rebellion" Part 3 accessed at: http://www.civilwararchive.com/Unreghst/unwiinf2.htm September 29, 2015.

Ellison, David. "The Civil War Draft in Plover and Steven's Point: A Study in Efforts: Attitudes, Frustrations and Results." *Portage County (Wisconsin) Historical Society*. Accessed at http://www.pchswi.org/archives/misc/cwdraft.html on September 7, 2015.

Estenson, Gene, "Chapter 2, The Norwegian Regiment in the Civil War." *Descendants of immigrants from the region of Telemark, Norway*. Telelaget of America: Copyright © 2009-2015. Accessed at: http://telelaget.com/pioneers/civilwar/regiment.htm on September 29, 2015.

Evans, Nicholas J. *Hands across the Sea*. "Migration from Northern Europe to America via Port of Hull, 1848-1914." Norway-Heritage, 1999. Accessed on 1-29-2016 at http://www.norwayheritage.com/articles/templates/voyages.asp?articleid=28&zoneid=6 .
Expositor 1881.

Find a Grave. https://www.findagrave.com/memorial/95207966/gunild-marie-hoen.

Folkedahl, Beulah. *Knud Knudsen and His America Book*. Norwegian-American Historical Society, Volume 23, accessed online at https://www.naha,stolafedu/pubs/nas/vlume23_5.html, 108.

Tanum Lutheran Parish Records for Bayview Parish. Microfilm records accessed at Tucson, Arizona through exchange with Salt Lake LDS History Center.

Geller, Jeffrey F. Women of the Asylum: Voices from Behind the Walls. 1840-1945, Anchor Books. (1994).

Gesme, Ann Urness. *Between Rocks and Hard Places.*
Minnesota: Caragana Press, 1993, 2004.

Gosz, Kathy. *Village Life in Kreis, Saarbarg, Germany. A Look at LeHavre, a Less-Known Port for German Immigrants. Accessed blog 6-25-2015*
at http://19thcenturyrhinelandlive.blogspot.com.

Hale, James B. "The US Mail comes to Door County." October 2013. Accessed at http://doorcounty.net/article-20364-door-county-history-the-us-mail-comes-to-door-county.html on 5-25-2017.

Hazen, Theodore R. "How the Roller Mills Changed the Milling Industry." Accessed on 4-2-2017 at
http://www.angelfire.com/journal/millrestoration/roller.html.

Historical Society of Idaho Springs. "Historical Events and People." Accessed on 6-28-2017 at
http://historicidahosprings.com/historical-events-and-people/.

Histories of Washington and Ozaukee Counties, Western Publishing, 1881, accessed through Wisconsin GenWeb project at
http://www.rootsweb.ancestry.com/~wiozauke/histories/Port.html.

History of Education in Norway. Norway Education. The Oslo Times. Norway, 2015-09-15. Accessed at
http://www.theoslotimes.com/article/history-of-education-in-norway on 11-19-2015.
History of Green Bay, http://www.ci.green-bay.wi.us/history/.

Hoffbeck, Steven R. *The Haymakers: A Chronicle of Five Farm Families.* Minnesota Historical Society 2000 Ebook ISBN 978-0-87351-736-2.

Holand, Hjalmar. "HAINESVILLE: An Old Seaman's Paradise." For *Skandinaven*, a Norwegian newspaper, 1922. Translated from Norwegian by Petra Haines Slotten, Redmond, Washington, 1977.

Holand, Hjalmar. *History of Door County, Vol I.*

Holand, Hjalmar. History of Sturgeon Bay, Door County, Wisconsin (Part I). From History of Door County, Wisconsin, The County Beautiful. The S.J. Clark Publishing Company. Chicago. 1917.

Holand, Hjalmar. *My First 80 Years.* Accessed through Google Books.

Holden Lutheran Church Records 1848-1909 for Berthe Marie Anderson, daughter of Halvor Anderson and Karen Henriksdatter Birth 16 October 1848 undated baptism. ALC Reel #485, Scan00.

Homestead Congress. *U.S. Land Laws*. Friends of Homestead National Monument of America. Accessed on 12-3-2015 at http://homesteadcongress.blogspot.com/2010/12/u-s-land-laws.html.
http://articles.baltimoresun.com/2003-10-10/news/0310100309_1_firestorm-chicago-fire-fire-museum.

Janus, Edward. *Creating Dairyland*. Audio production Chris Bocast for Divergent Arts Ltd. Wisconsin Historical Society Press. Copyright 2012.

Jenkins, Ann and Weir, Maggie. *Images of America: Sturgeon Bay*. For the Door County Historical Museum. Charleston, N.C. Arcadia Publishing 2006.

Kincheloe, John W. III, "Earliest American Explorers: Adventure and Survival." *Tar Heel Junior Historian.*

Copyright North Carolina Museum of History. Accessed at
http://www.ncpedia.org/history/early/contact on 12-29-2016.

Kiviat, Erik. *Vegetation of Duchess, N.Y.* Accessed at:
www.hudsonrivervalley.org/review/pdfs/hvrr_1pt2_kiviat.pdf
on 2016-09-22.

Lawrence County - Crows Peak.pdf Provenance unknown.
LDS History Center: Tanum Lutheran Church Parish Records

Lovell, Odd S. "Norwegian Americans: Cuisine." Accessed at
http://www.everyculture.com/multi/Le-Pa/Norwegian-
Americans.html.

Lovoll, Odd S. *The Promise of America: A History of the
Norwegian-American People*, Minneapolis, University of
Minnesota Press, in cooperation with The Norwegian-
American Historical Association, 1984.

Lyons, Christian Matthew. The Deadliest Forest Fire in
American History: The Great Peshtigo Fire of 1871. Thesis for
partial fulfillment of Masters of Arts in Emergency and
Disaster Management. America Public University System, W.
Virginia, 2011.

Manning, J.R. *The Worst Fire in America History.* Accessed at
http://landmarkhunter.com/180472-peshtigo-fire-cemetery/.

Mansfeld, J.B., ed. "An Interesting Description of the Lakes in
1847 - Thurlow Weed's Enjoyable Trip." *History of the Great
Lakes.* Vol. I Ch. 36: 1841-1850. 1846 Accessed at
http://www.maritimehistoryofthegreatlakes.ca/documents/hgl/d
efault.asp?ID=s040.

Marcy, Randolph, *The Prairie Traveler.* New York: Harper &
Brothers, 1861. 40. Accessed at

https://ia800202.us.archive.org/32/items/prairietravelerh01mar
c/prairietravelerh01marc.pdf.

Marriage Certificate between Nelly Olenia Holvotson (sic) and
Isaac U. Chase. Provided by Margaret Chase Gibbons to Adie
Hegrenes Haines 1985.

Martin, Charles R. "Otumba" [Sturgeon Bay]. *History of Door
County, Wisconsin.*

Martin, Chas R. History of Door County: The Great Fire, The
Expositor 1881.

Megan Margino, Megan. *The Arm That Clutched the Torch:
The Statue of Liberty's Campaign for a Pedestal.* Milstein
Division of U.S. History. Local History & Genealogy. Stephen
A. Schwarzman Building April 7, 2015. Accessed at
https://www.nypl.org/blog/2015/04/07/statue-liberty-pedestal
on 2-12-2017.

Moravian Church in North America. "A Brief History of the
Moravian Church." Accessed at http://www.moravian.org/the-
moravian-church/history/.

Morton, T.G. "Removal of the Ovaries as a Cure for Insanity."
American Journal of Insanity 49 (1892).
Naeseth, Gerhard B., Blaine Hedberg, ed. *Norwegian
Immigrants to the United States. A Biographical Directory
1825-1850* Volume Two 1844-1846. Deborah, Iowa,
Vesterheim Norwegian-American Museum. Anundsen
Publishing Co, 1997.

Nicolet, Jean, T*he Encyclopedia Britanicca*, Published 10-23-
2013. Accessed at
http://www.pchswi.org/archives/misc/cwdraft.html on
September 7, 2015.

Noltze, Kathy. *Ulao: Footsteps on the Bluff.* Arizona: Property Purveyer. 2011.

Numbers, Ronald L and Judith Walzer Levit., *Wisconsin Medicine: Historical Perspective*. University of Wisconsin Press, 1981.

Passenger Ships and Images: Ancestry.com, 2007.

Paul, D.B. and Spencer H.G. "It's Ok, We're Not Cousins by Blood: The Cousin Marriage Controversy in Historical Perspective." 2008. Accessed at PLoS Biol 6(12): e320. doi:10.1371/journal.pbio.0060320.

Peninsula Genealogical Society. Schools. "Town of Sturgeon Bay" Accessed at http://www.rootsweb.ancestry.com/~wipgs/PGS/TownofSturgeonBay.htm 10-24-15.

Pennsylvania Hospital Newsletter of the Friends of the Hospital in Historic Asylums of America accessed by author on 3-26-2017 at http://www.rootsweb.ancestry.com/~asylums/.

Perlman, Sam. "The First Door County Residents." *Door County Living*. 2006-09-01. accessed at https://doorcountypulse.com/the-first-door-county-residents/.

Preuss, Linka. *Linka 1829-1880 - Linka's diary: A Norwegian Immigrant Story in Word and Sketches.* Minneapolis, Minnesota: Lutheran University Press, 2008.

Price, Mary Jane Frances, *The history of Port Washington, in Ozaukee County, Wisconsin.* De Paul University (1943) Accessed at http://digital.library.wisc.edu/1711.dl/WI.OzHistPortWash.

Priebe, Henry Jr. "The City of Buffalo 1840-1850." *The History of Buffalo, NY* accessed at http://history.buffalonet.org/1840-50.html.

Richter, Conrad. *The Fields.* 1946. Knopf, Alfred A. 1991.

Sadler, Jo Anne, *Early Norwegian Immigrants on the Erie Canal*, 2008. Norway-Heritage - Hands Across the Sea website by Solem, Børge. Accessed at http://www.norwayheritage.com/articles/templates/voyages.asp?articleid=150&zoneid=6.

Sea Distances / Port Distances - online tool for calculation distances between sea ports. Accessed October 22, 2015 www.sea-distances.org.

Semmingsen, Ingrid Gustad. Norwegian Emigration to America in the 19th Century.Volume XI.

Semmingsen, Ingrid. *Norway to America: A History of the Migration.* Minneapolis: University of Minnesota Press, 1978. Translated by Einar Haugen.

Sims, Hugh Joffre, *Sims' History of Elgin County, Volume III,* Alymer, Ontario, Canada, 1986.

Stiles, T.J. *The First Tycoon: The Epic Life of Cornelius Vanderbilt.* New York: Alfred A. Knopf. 2009.

Tasker, G. *Worst fire largely unknown.* The Baltimore Sun, 2003-10-10.

The Immigration Process at Castle Garden (1871). Gjenvick-Gjønvik Archives: Social and Cultural History - The Future of Our Past. Accessed at http://www.gjenvick.com/Immigration/CastleGarden/1871-TheImmigrationProcessAtCastleGarden.html.

The McGuffey Readers - 1836 version. Accessed on 11-06-2015 at http://www.mcguffeyreaders.com/1836_original.htm.

The Wisconsin Logging Book, 1839-1939 Accessed online at McMillan Memorial Library on 9-3-2015.

Thonne, Lynette, compiler. "Walk in the Footsteps." *The Hanson House and Family Story. 1856-2014.*

To Soldiers Killed on Active Duty. Memorial Day--May 28, 2007, Adie Hegrenes, Sturgeon Bay, WI.

Town of Brussels, Door County Wisconsin: About the Town. Copyright @ 2015   Accessed at http://www.townofbrussels.com on September 29, 2015.

Town of Gardner, Door County, Wisconsin. Accessed at http://www.townofgardner.org on September 30, 2015.

U.S. Department of Veterans Affairs. National Cemetery Administration - Corinth National Cemetery. Accessed online at http://www.cem.va.gov/cems/nchp/corinth.asp on 1-8-2017.

United States Army: Inventory of Effects of Deceased Soldier.

United States Dept of the Interior. National Register of Historic Places Inventory - Nomination Form for Peshtigo Fire Cemetery. Accessed on on 1-6-2010 at http://focus.nps.gov/pdfhost/docs/NRHP/Text/70000037.pdf

US Department of State: Office of the Historian. Home › Milestones › 1866–1898 Chinese Immigration and the Chinese Exclusion Acts. Accessed at https://history.state.gov/milestones/1866-1898/chinese-immigration on 2-18-2016.

Weed, Thurlow. *An Interesting Description of the Lakes in 1847.* Accessed online Google Books 10-18-2016.

Wells, Robert W. *Fire at Peshtigo.* Prentice-Hall, inc. Englewood Cliffs, N.J. 1968.

Wikipedia contributors, "Green Bay, Wisconsin." *Wikipedia, The Free Encyclopedia.* http://en.wikipedia.org/w/index.php?title=Green_Bay,_Wisconsin&oldid=641018258 (accessed January 7, 2015).

Wikipedia contributors, "Treaty of Washington, with Menominee (1831)." *Wikipedia, The Free Encyclopedia.* https://en.wikipedia.org/w/index.php?title=Treaty_of_Washington,_with_Menominee_(1831)&oldid=763654705 (accessed January 29, 2018).

Wilder, Laura Ingalls. Garth Williams, illus. *Little House on the Prairie.* New York, Harper & Row, 1935.

Williams, Michael. "The Living Tractor." *No Beasts for draught but Oxen.* Accessed at http://www.foxearth.org.uk/oxen.html.

Wilma, David and Walt Crowley. "Tacoma — Thumbnail History." 2003. HistoryLink.org Essay 5055, [Essay corrected on June 25, 2006, and corrected and expanded on May 4, 2015]. Accessed March 3, 2016.

Wilson, Aaste, "Live blant nybyggjarane [Life Among the Settlers], quoted in *Telesoga"* September 1917. Quoted in *Norwegian Americans* by Odd S. Lovell accessed at http://www.everyculture.com/multi/Le-Pa/Norwegian-Americans.html on 1-3-2017

Wilson, Henn. *Wilson's Illustrated Guide to the Hudson River*, New York: H. Wilson, 1850, Google Books.

Wisconsin Department of Health and Family Services. *Wisconsin Vital Record Index, pre-1907.* Madison, WI, USA. Wisconsin Historical Society. Wisconsin Historical Society Library Archives. Marriage License. vol 1, p 258. Ancestry.com.

Women's Right to Vote in Norway. Accessed on 2-16-17 at http://www.norway.az/norwayandcountry/Political-Affairs/Womens-Right-to-Vote-in-Norway-1913-2013/#.WKYHXBiZPdQ.

Women's Rights Timeline. Leonor Annenberg Institute for Civics. accessed at http://www.annenbergclassroom.org/Files/Documents/Timelines/WomensRightstimeline.pdf on 2-15-2017.

Woodcock, Thomas S. "1836 trip from Schenectady, New York to Buffalo." *Traveling the Erie Canal, 1836*, Eye Witness to History, accessed at www.eyewitnesstohistory.com (2004).

Young, Beth Robertson. *Old Idlewild.* The Peninsula Volume 14, 2007-2008.

INDEX

A -

The Advocate. See also Door County Advocate
   on Helene's funeral, 287
   on Idlewild tourist resort, 279
   on Tallak and Maria's separation, 283–284
   Tallak's death notice, 291–292
   on Tallak's old age, 282, 288–291
Ahnapee and Western Railway, 277–278
Allen, Thomas S., 46
Allouez, Father, 121
Amundsdatter, Marte Karine (1859-1865), 100, 142
Amundsdatter, Marte Karine (1866-). See Haines, Carrie
Andersdatter, Ingeborg, 28
Anderson, Albert, 238
Anderson, Anne Elise, 61
Anderson, Berthe Marie, 61, 62
Anderson, Halvor, 61
Anderson, Karen Henriksdatter, 28, 60–62
Anderson, Kirsten Halvorsdatter (1825-)
   Canada–Port Ulio move (1848), 56, 58–60
   in emigration journey (1846), 26, 33, 38
   emigration preparation, 8, 13, 16
   at family reunion (1882), 202–203
   marriage and children, 60, 61, 73, 74
   in Port Ulio area, 61, 68–69, 71, 73, 74, 204, 244
   and Soren Anderson, 33, 60, 73
Anderson, Mary Jane, 73
Anderson, Soren, 33, 60, 73, 204
Anundsen, Tellif, 64
Appleton's General Guide to the United States and Canada
   (1881), 215–217, 215f, 222
Arnesplass (farm), 97–100, 142–143

Clay Banks, WI, 161, 175, 262
clothing. See also sewing
    on arrival in New York City, 38
    for Carrie's wedding, 254–255
    in Civil War period, 111–112
    footwear on wagon journeys, 81
cold, of January 1888, 250
Colorado, 151, 261
confirmation, 97, 172
consumption, 230, 276
Corinth National Cemetery (MS), 116
Corvisier, André, 22–23
Court, Henry, 177
cousin marriage, 258, 261
covered wagons, 76, 79–80
croup, 275, 276
Crows Peak, DT, 177
Cunard Line, 198

D
dairy farming, 269–270
Dakota Territory (DT)
    Eli in (1881-), 188, 212, 218, 237
    Lizzie in (1886-1888), 233, 236, 237, 240, 241, 245–246,
        258, 262
    Oscar's letters from (1887), 235–244, 235f
    Tallak in (1877-1878), 177
    Tellif in (1877-1880), 177–178, 185
    Tellif in (1886-1887), 232–234, 236, 237, 240, 241, 244
    Tellif in (1888), 255, 258, 262
Daniels, E.C., 289
Danker, Harry, interview with Mary Haines (1935). See family
        stories, by Mary Haines
Deadwood, DT
    Lizzie in (1886-1888), 233, 236, 237, 245, 258, 262
    Oscar's letters from (1887), 235–244, 235f
    Tallak and Tellif in (1877-1878), 177, 233
    Tellif in (1886-1887), 232–234, 236, 237, 240
    women in, 245–246

Isaksen, Lars, 8, 11
Island #10, battle of (1862), 109

J
Jacobson, Theodore, 250
Jensen, Kate and Con, 248
Jensen, Mary, 257
Jenson, John, 257
Johnson, President Andrew, 147

K
Kansas, 261
Kirkbridge, Dr. Thomas Story, 247
Kirkbridge state hospital, 247
Knickerbocker Ice Company, 277
Knudtson, Knudt
    death of (1885), 231
    after Ellen's death (1880-1881), 188–190
    and Idlewild land, 176, 188, 189, 212–213
    journey to Bamble (1880), 181, 182
    marriage to Mary, 151
Knudtson, Mary Haines. See Haines, Mary (Aunt Mary)

L
Lake Erie
    journey to (1846), 39, 43, 45–48, 51
    journeys on (1840s), 48–49, 54–55, 58–59
land, of Door County vs. Bamble, 144
Land Act of 1824, 138
land clearing
    after Peshtigo Fire (1871), 168
    in Port Ulio (1840s), 67–68
    in Sugar Creek (1850s), 89–91
land dealings
    of Ellen, 129, 136, 138
    of family members, 138
    for Haines Brothers enterprise, 211–212

Made in the USA
Columbia, SC
20 November 2018